SLIM CUISINE: QUICK AND EASY

Also by Sue Kreitzman

Cambridge Slim Cuisine
Cambridge Slim Cuisine: A Second Helping
The Complete Slim Cuisine
The Cambridge Slim Cuisine Diet
Slim Cuisine: Indulgent Desserts
Slim Cuisine: Italian Style

SUE KREITZMAN

Slim Cuisine: Quick and Easy

A Manual of Healthy Eating for a World with too much Fat, and too Little Time

LONDON NEW YORK SYDNEY TORONTO

This edition published 1993 by,
BCA
by arrangement with Bantam Press
a division of Transworld Publishers Ltd

CN 6632

Printed and bound in Great Britain by
Mackays of Chatham PLC, Chatham, Kent

For my son Shawm, who – despite a frantic schedule, and what may be the tiniest kitchen in Chelsea – regularly turns out a perfectly gorgeous array of Quick and Easy Slim Cuisine with the greatest of ease.

Contents

Acknowledgements

This is my seventh Slim Cuisine book and – at this point – I feel that I am conducting a very personal and lively conversation with countless readers throughout the country. I must thank all of you who write me heartwarming letters, and come to see me at cookery demonstrations in order to listen, to learn, to offer suggestions, and to explain how Slim Cuisine has changed your lives. You inspire me, and keep my enthusiasm alive.

I am grateful to Dr Stephen Kreitzman (Dr Husband), and The Howard Foundation for their support of, and ongoing belief in, the importance of my work.

My agent, David Grossman, and the 'Bantam Bunch', Ursula Mackenzie, Broo Doherty, Helenka Fuglewicz, Lizzie Laczynska, Alison Barrow and Deanna Larson-Whiterod, continue to make my professional life a pleasure.

Sue Atkinson, with the help of Carol Handslip, has – again – brought my collection of recipes to vivid, photographic life. I am constantly amazed at how Sue listens to my ideas about ambience and mood, and then brings it all to life, far beyond my expectations. She is a formidable talent and a privilege to work with.

My assistant Sandie Michel-King, and my secretary Rosie Espley, as well as helpers Brenda Huebler and Mary Hardy, keep things moving along efficiently (Sandie has the organizational abilities of an admiral, when we put the Slim Cuisine show on the road) and they all help maintain the warm and friendly work environment in which I thrive.

And finally, a happy and loving thank you to my son Shawm, who has learned the basics so well and has developed his own (spicy) culinary flair, and to his friend Friedericke Mussgnug, who has been so eager to learn: you are both *so much fun* to have around the kitchen!

Introduction

This book is about real life. It's about long days filled with large and small frustrations, too many things to do, responsibilities to work and family pulling simultaneously in all directions. It's about supermarkets never being open when you really need them, so that food shopping seems to be a constant mad dash into hordes of crazed, trolley-wielding, equally frustrated fellow shoppers. It's about frazzled nerves, mental and physical exhaustion, and deep hunger at the end of those long days, and family members – suffering from similar exhaustion and hunger – waiting to be fed.

How does one deal with this combination of hunger, exhaustion, responsibility (and – all too often – guilt)? Fish and chips, take-aways of all descriptions, fast-food restaurants, pizza delivered to your door by motor bike, shelf-stable packets, upmarket chilled dishes and frozen meals briefly warmed in the microwave – all these are temporary solutions to the never-ending problem. But not only are these solutions temporary, they are profoundly unsatisfying as well. Packet meals, take-aways and so on fill the empty void for a time, but they fill that void with some anonymous corporation's idea of food, of flavourings, of nutrition (or lack of it). Relying on such meals robs a family of something very special: the planning, the cooking, the sharing of *personal* food.

11

There is nothing quite as satisfying as eating meals you want to eat, seasoned the way you like them, in exactly the quantities you feel able to eat. The fast-food industry is in the business of feeding a vast, collective palate. Subsisting on such food reduces mealtimes to a mindless exercise with none of the sustaining emotional pleasure that real home-cooking can bring. And if you are dedicated to a low-fat, high-nutrient diet as well as a personally delicious and comforting one, it is very unlikely that anonymous fast food, whether it comes from a supermarket, a burger bar, or a High Street take-away, is going to meet your requirements.

So what do you do when you love good food, glowing health and radiant slimness, but have little *time* for serious kitchen activity? Are you stuck with the food industry's depressing array of high-fat, high-salt, high-sugar, low-taste choices? With this collection of recipes, techniques and advice I hope to enable you to take control and prepare gorgeous home-cooked, low-fat meals and snacks with a minimum of fuss, mess or advance preparation. Workday meals, family feasts, even dinner parties in all their glory: all of these can be achieved without an investment of hours of your time. This book is a compendium of shopping strategies, advice on stocking your larder and freezer, and clean-up short cuts, as well as fast techniques and recipes. Why should busy people have to suffer with commercial rubbish? Pamper yourself, but don't compromise your schedule. Welcome to the fast lane!

About Slim Cuisine

I've been writing cookbooks since the mid-seventies but – until the mid-eighties they all were (for want of a better phrase) 'Fat Cuisine'. That's really how I got into trouble in the first place. Food was my profession, my passion, my preoccupation, my obsession. If you were to open one of my pre-1982 Fat Cuisine books, the butter, oil and cream would practically ooze from the pages on to your lap. No wonder I eventually tipped the scale at 15½ stone. Had I not finally put on the brakes, taken things into my own hands, forcefully thrown off the yoke of traditional gastronomy, I would undoubtedly have continued my out-of-control 'personal growth' until even the roomiest tent dress was too snug, the widest door was too narrow, the sturdiest chair was too fragile for my ever-billowing bulk.

In 1982, when I lost a considerable amount of weight, I realized that if I wanted to stay slim *and* continue wallowing in my foodie passion, I would have to do something drastic, so I did. I set out to reinvent cuisine. I have to sauté my onions in butter or oil in order to give my recipes depth of flavour? Hah! Sez who? I need cream for sauces, fat for pastries, ghee for curries, olive oil or mayonnaise for salads? Oh yeah? Whose behind is it anyway? Whose thighs, tummy, chin, waistline, cheekbones? They're mine, and I'm going to keep them in good shape, in spite of the exhortations of our fattening society, but I'm double-damned if I have to eat boring food, count Calories or starve in order to do so.

My food-writing career and my wholehearted enjoyment of food has continued to flourish despite those departed six stones, but I write 'Slim Cuisine' now: I bid very good riddance to 'Fat Cuisine'. Slim Cuisine is *my* way of cookery: new culinary techniques, a low-fat gastronomic philosophy and an ever increasing collection of recipes that allow feasting, enjoyment, freedom from Calorie counting, even frequent 'therapeutic binge-ing', without the usual inevitable galloping *schmaltz* (and without the usual health problems) associated with over-eating and over-consumption of fats. With Slim Cuisine, I'm doing something for myself (I'll *never* be fat again and, as Scarlett O'Hara said, I'll never be hungry again either) and I'm doing something for all the others who want to live a long healthy life of slimness *and* gastronomic hedonism.

The Guidelines

The principle of Slim Cuisine is simple: axe all added fat and all high-fat foods from your diet. Fat contains more than twice the Calories of carbohydrate and protein; Calories that are metabolized in a way that actually make you fatter, faster, than carbohydrate and protein Calories. If you devote yourself to a no-added-fat diet, weight *maintenance* is never a problem – and weight *loss* is ridiculously simple and painless.

BANISH THESE FOODS

The Obvious Fats

Butter	Dripping
All oils	Lard
Solid shortenings	Suet
Margarine	Poultry fat
'Low-fat' spreads	Poultry skin
Vegetable shortenings	Bacon fat

Full-fat and semi-skimmed milk products including full-fat and semi-skimmed hard cheese, soft cheeses, yoghurts, fromage frais, cottage cheese, cream, soured cream, clotted cream, etc. (The very low-fat versions [less than 1 per cent fat] of these products can be eaten freely [see below] and medium-fat Parmesan and medium-fat mozzarella cheese may be used occasionally during weight maintenance.)
Mayonnaise and salad dressings
Fatty meats

The Less Obvious Fats

Cut these out as well:
All nuts (except chestnuts, which are not high in fat)
Egg yolks – the whites are fine. On weight maintenance, if your blood cholesterol is normal, it won't hurt to have the occasional whole egg. On weight loss, avoid the yolks altogether.
Avocados
Coconut

The Hidden Fats

Eliminate, as well, all prepared foods, from frozen foods to baked goods to snacks and convenience food, and everything in between, that contain added fat. Read labels!

Use these products lavishly in place of full-fat and semi-skimmed dairy products:
Skimmed milk yoghurt
Skimmed milk fromage frais
Buttermilk cultured from skimmed milk
Skimmed milk quark or curd cheese
Skimmed milk
Skimmed milk powder

Fat Note

A *no-fat* diet is not easy to achieve, nor should anyone attempt to do so. The human body needs a small amount of fat to function. If you eat a full range of Slim Cuisine dishes, the panoply of lean meats, fish, poultry, grains, vegetables and fruit they lavishly provide, will keep your body stoked up with the essential fat it needs – *added* fats are certainly not needed.

Low-Fat For Life

Following a low-fat, high-nutrition diet will help to keep you slim and healthy, but how can a very low-fat diet keep you *happy* if you love good food? Isn't low-fat food boring, tasteless, almost impossible to eat day in, day out, for a lifetime?

Listen carefully please: Slim Cuisine – quick, lean and healthy though it is – is NO COMPROMISE! It is *good food* in its own right. You will *not* suffer deprivation – it is REAL FOOD! Hold on. Let me calm down. Why am I so excited? Because I get angry with gastronomic types who believe that there is only one way to cook *real* food, and that is with plenty of the classic oils, fats and high-fat dairy products; who believe that very low-fat versions of the food of the world are – by definition – cheats, fakes, pale imitations *and not delicious*; who believe that we either eat such food the way it was *meant* to be eaten (with off-the-scale fat levels) or not at all; who, therefore, condemn us fat-prone folks to a miserable, guilt-ridden life of overweight, of yo-yo weight gains and losses, of eating disorders. Don't let such hidebound, totally out-of-date, blind prejudice stop you from axing the fat from your diet. It may not be *fashionable* in the foodie world to avoid olive oil or butter. It may seem strange to others who learn about nutrition through magazine and television adverts that you avoid even margarine and 'low-fat' spreads, that you *never* butter your bread, or dollop cream on to your berries. But follow low-fat precepts and you will – despite their scorn – find yourself enjoying your food as you have never done in your life. The *guilt* will be gone. The constant *weight gain* will be gone. And – how wonderful this is – you will taste food as it has never tasted before, because the blunting veil of *fat* will be gone. Food will taste – at last – of itself. Creamy foods will be creamy but not cloying; puréed vegetable soups will taste like essence of their vegetables (even when made with frozen vegetables); mushrooms and potatoes will taste of mushrooms and potatoes and not lashings of grease. And chocolate! Well I leave it to you to discover just how intense and seductive chocolate desserts can be without added fat.

You don't need a restaurant kitchen or the dexterity of a professional to cope with my new-wave, low-fat, fast-food techniques. These techniques are for fat-prone home cooks with keen taste-buds, deep hungers and limited time. I consider myself the patron saint of such individuals. This book is meant to be a manual of healthy gastronomic survival for a world that contains too much fat and too little time.

15

Stocking The Kitchen

In my quest for recipes that are fast and easy, yet very low in fat and a pleasure to eat as well, I have – for this book – ventured further into convenience food than ever before. By convenience food I mean ingredients in cans, jars and packets . . . *frozen* food – things I was prepared to hate, but thought should be tried, just to make sure. There were plenty of convenience foods that I found quite unacceptable but there were some big surprises too. Frozen vegetables, for instance – frozen sweet corn is amazingly good, as are frozen peas. Some frozen vegetables (cauliflower for example) lose some texture as a result of the freezing process, but that doesn't matter if they are puréed into a creamy soup, or simmered into a hearty stew – the flavour remains surprisingly fresh. Frozen fish amazed me as well – it can be very good. The collection of recipes and techniques in this book teach you how to use certain convenience foods – canned, boxed, frozen – to your advantage.

The following lists encompass useful ingredients to have on hand at all times in your store cupboard, fridge and freezer. With such bounty on hand you will never be at a loss for something wonderful to cook. Store-cupboard and freezer staples can be purchased in quantity every few months. Refrigerator staples need to be purchased at shorter intervals, and used while they are at their peak.

Store–Cupboard Staples

Wines and Spirits

Red vermouth
White vermouth
Dry sherry
Dry red wine

Medium-dry cider
Dark rum
Cointreau or grand marnier
Calvados

Note: all of these wines and spirits are optional – nice to have for some recipes, but certainly not essential.

Vinegars

Balsamic vinegar
Sherry wine vinegar

Red or white wine vinegar
Cider vinegar

Carbohydrate Corner
(Pasta, Grains, Flours, etc.)

Assorted pasta
Couscous
Quick-cooking polenta (see Mail
Order Guide, page 191)
Instant potatoes
Self-raising sponge flour

Self-raising brown flour
Strong white flour
Stone-ground wholewheat flour
Cornflour
Potatoes

Canned Vegetables

Artichoke hearts in
brine
Red peppers (pimientos)
Creamed corn
Sweetcorn kernels
Chillies

Canned beans & pulses:
Black-eyed beans
Borlotti beans
Cannellini beans
Red kidney beans
Chick peas

Dairy Products

Skimmed milk
powder

Longlife skimmed milk in
½-litre boxes

Sweeteners

Mild runny honey
Molasses
Light brown sugar

Castor sugar
Granulated NutraSweet

Tomato Products

Sun-dried tomatoes (dry pack),
(see Mail Order Guide,
page 191)
Canned whole Italian tomatoes
Canned chopped Italian
tomatoes

Tomato purée
Tomato passata (comes in boxes,
cans or bottles)
Tomato juice (preferably in
boxes)

Chutneys & Pickles, etc.

Capers
Mango chutney
Apple-Mango chutney

Curried fruit chutney
Tuscan lemon chutney
Lime chilli pickle

Jams & Dried Fruit

Ready-to-eat dried figs
Ready-to-eat pitted prunes
Dried apricots
Dried apple rings
Dried pears
Dried cake fruit
Raisins
Sultanas
Low-sugar jams:
Cherry
Apricot
Strawberry

Miscellaneous

Tuna in water or brine
Low-salt, low-fat vegetable stock
(bouillon) powder, (see Mail
Order Guide, page 191)
Tiny orange lentils
Plain, unseasoned breadcrumbs
Low-fat, unsweetened cocoa
powder (see Mail Order
Guide, page 191)
Crystallized ginger
Store-bought meringue shells
Amaretti biscuits
Cream of tartar

Flavour Vegetables

Onions
Garlic
Ginger

Dried Herbs, Spices & Aromatics

Salt
Whole black peppercorns
Dried oregano
Dried tarragon
Whole nutmegs
Ground mace
Ground cinnamon
Ground coriander
Ground cayenne pepper
Ground Hungarian paprika
Crushed dried chilli
Caraway seeds
Anise or fennel seeds
Poppy and sesame seeds (best to
keep these two in the fridge
or freezer – see page 21)
Five spice powder
Mustard seeds
Vanilla beans

Liquid Seasonings & Sauces

Teriyaki sauce
Soy sauce
Hoisin sauce
Chinese chilli sauce
Worcestershire sauce
Tandoori paste
Tabasco sauce
Dijon mustard
Natural vanilla essence

Freezer Staples

Dairy Products
(These freeze very well, so you can stock up in quantity)

Medium-fat Italian-style
mozzarella cheese
Grated Parmesan cheese

Quark or no-fat curd cheese
Buttermilk

Fish

Frozen cod fillets
Frozen haddock fillets
Frozen lemon sole fillets

Frozen tiny shelled prawns
Frozen smoked cod

Fruit

Orange juice concentrate
Frozen unsweetened raspberries
Frozen unsweetened
strawberries
Frozen orange and grapefruit
sections

Frozen melon balls
*(also keep in the freezer whole
oranges [see page 167] and
bags of fruit cubes and
berries [see page 171] that
you have frozen yourself.)*

Vegetables

Sweetcorn (extra sweet)
Peas (petit pois & garden)
Broad beans
Cauliflower florets
Cabbage
Spinach

Carrots
Swedes
Green beans
Sliced peppers
Broccoli

Stocks (see page 21)

Fish stock

Chicken stock

Refrigerator Staples

Baguette dough in tubes (see
page 163)
Free-range eggs
No-fat fromage frais
Italian-style, medium fat
mozzarella cheese
Grated Parmesan cheese
Quark or no-fat curd cheese

Buttermilk
Vacuum-packed beetroot in
natural juice
Fresh herbs
Spring onions
Lemons
Limes
Oranges

Advice on Ingredients

Bacon

I like to use thin slices of well-trimmed, lean back bacon here and there as a seasoning: a bit of smoked bacon imparts a hauntingly smoky edge to many dishes. Those who don't eat pork, or who don't eat meat at all, or who should keep their salt levels down, can leave it out entirely. The smokiness will be gone, but the dish will still taste just fine.

Balsamic Vinegar

This very special vinegar is produced in Modena, Italy. It is made from boiling the must of Trebbiano di Spagno grapes until it thickens and caramelizes, then culturing it in wooden barrels. The finished Balsamic vinegar – the real stuff – is very expensive, and complex and mellow enough to drink out of a glass. Many supermarkets now carry inexpensive Balsamic vinegars, factory-made rather than cottage-produced in the traditional wood-cask manner. But even these inexpensive Balsamic vinegars are very good, with a mellow, sweet taste; very useful in no-fat salad dressings.

Fresh Tomatoes

The only way (unless you grow them yourself) to have tomatoes that taste like tomatoes is to plan ahead. Buy firm tomatoes (try to avoid hothouse tomatoes – the ones grown out of doors are best) and store them, at room temperature (a cool part of the room) in a paper bag, with a ripe banana closed in with the tomatoes. In a few days to a week, the tomatoes will have developed real tomato flavour. (The banana will be *very* ripe as well, perfect for Banana Milk Pudding [see page 180].) On the other hand, cherry tomatoes *do* taste like tomatoes, especially if you let them sit at room temperature for a day or two. Don't bother trying to skin cherry tomatoes, they are too small and fiddly, but ordinary tomatoes can be skinned quickly. Put a few tomatoes in a bowl, pour boiling water over them, allow them to sit for 10 seconds, then pour off the water. Cut the stem out of each one and slip off the skins. To seed the tomatoes, cut in half and scoop out the seeds with your finger.

Herbs

With very few exceptions, I don't like dried herbs. There is really no comparison between the fresh and the dried. The judicious use of fresh herbs can change a simple dish from the mundane to the sublime. Fresh parsley is easily obtainable all the year round from most supermarkets, as well as coriander, mint, chives and basil. Substitution is often possible if a particular fresh herb is unavailable. Parsley can often stand in for other herbs; basil and mint are related and can usually stand in for one another, and minced spring onions can take the place of chives. It is best not to substitute dried for fresh; either leave it out or use some parsley. An exception is tarragon. Dried tarragon is consistently excellent if used properly. Properly means that you crumble it between your fingers to release the flavour components; don't use too much of it, and never sprinkle it dry on anything; use it with liquid – in dressings, infusions or sauces. Dried oregano can also be useful in flavour infusions, but sniff it first; when it goes musty and old, it's awful.

Passata

Passata (sieved tomatoes), sometimes called 'creamed tomatoes', are sold in boxes, cans or jars, and make a convenient base for any number of instant tomato sauces. If you can't find passata, cream tomatoes yourself by blending an equivalent amount of canned, chopped Italian tomatoes, and then pushing the purée through a sieve.

Sesame Seeds and Poppy Seeds

Although both of these seeds have a very high oil content, I like them as a topping for loaves of home-made bread. Used in this way, they add delightful texture and flavour to bread, but the amount used is miniscule, so you will not compromise your diet. Because of the oil content, both seeds go rancid quickly. To prevent this, store them in the refrigerator or freezer.

Stock

Many of the savoury Slim Cuisine recipes begin with a flavourful infusion: a mixture of garlic, diced sun-dried tomatoes (if you choose to use them), sliced spring onions and an optional pinch of dried chilli flakes simmered in stock until the garlic, tomatoes and onions are tender and the mixture is syrupy. This infusion and its variations are used instead of the usual (fattening!)

method of sautéing onions and garlic in butter or oil. What kind of stock to use? Home-made chicken and vegetable stocks are splendid, if you are in the habit of preparing them, but, these days, few people have time for such time-consuming kitchen activity. Fortunately, there are plenty of options.

1   Friggs Vegetal: The label on this vegetable bouillon powder indicates that it is meant to be used as a hot vegetable drink, but it makes a wonderful stock for cooking. It is not even necessary to reconstitute the powder first; simply combine the flavour ingredients (onions, garlic, etc.) in a frying pan, add water and sprinkle in a pinch or two of Vegetal. If you can't find Friggs Vegetal in the supermarket or health food shop (distribution tends to be spotty) it is available through mail order (see page 191).

2   There are other low-fat, low-salt stock powders and cubes available – check out your local health food store. Always read the fine print to make sure you are buying one that really *is* low in fat and salt – then try them out and see which pleases you.

3   Fresh stocks: chicken, vegetable and fish stocks are sold in half-pint pots in the chill section of many supermarkets. If you wish to buy them in quantity, and you have a big freezer, they will keep for months.

4   If you are out of both frozen stock and bouillon powder you can substitute a mixture of water and dry white wine or dry white vermouth for the stock, or – if necessary – just plain water.

Sun-dried Tomatoes

Almost exactly what they say (they are actually *air* dried, rather than sun-dried) – sun-dried tomatoes are like raisins made out of tomatoes rather than grapes. They are available jarred in oil, or dry in cellophane packets. For Slim Cuisine dry packed are the ones to use (they are available in Italian Delis, speciality food shops, or by Mail Order, see page 191). Sun-dried tomatoes have a deep and vivid taste. Snip three or four of them with scissors into a sauce, soup or casserole to give a lovely depth of flavour. They are an optional ingredient: if you can't find them leave them out, but if you do decide to use them, I think that you will be delighted with the wonderful flavour dimension they will give to your low-fat dishes.

Oven Advice

Know Your Oven

In all recipes involving the oven, cooking times are approximate. I'm always amazed at the inconsistency of cooking time between one oven and another. It depends upon many factors. Is it a gas oven or an electric one? Small or large? Is it fan-assisted? Are you using the top or the bottom shelf, are you baking one item only, or is the oven chock-full? Is the oven's thermostat working properly? You will learn the idiosyncrasies of your particular oven and your particular cooking situation quickly enough, but the first time out for any recipe will always be a 'test drive'. If a recipe states: cook for 30–35 minutes until just done, your oven may do it in 20, 25 or 40 minutes. That first try will establish what is correct for you. Make a note of it, so you don't have to guess the second time round.

Microwave Ovens

For a long time, I refused to own a microwave and considered it an anti-cuisine type of machine. *Real* cooks like me, I thought, don't fool around with things like that. Oh, how wrong I was! The microwave is one of the great kitchen inventions of our time. It's not just that it cooks *quickly*; it cooks in a completely different manner from conventional ovens. With the microwave, you can prepare – in a very little time – a broad spectrum of very low-fat recipes: creamy sauces, fudgy tortes, rich-tasting puddings, perfectly cooked fish, crisp-tender vegetables. It's not only that these dishes would take *longer* without the microwave, some of them would not even be possible. The problem I have with microwave ovens is that there is little consistency between individual ovens. I have tested the microwave recipes in this collection in a variety of different machines in an attempt to find some standard of performance. The wattage of the oven, of course, makes a difference. The size of the oven cavity makes a difference. Sometimes two supposedly identical ovens – same make, same size, same wattage – will give different results. There are charts available that give general advice on cooking times for microwave ovens of varying wattage, but I find that – given the wild fluctuations of performance possible from machine to machine – such charts are not reliable. You will soon understand the peculiarities of your own particular machine. Remember: in all microwave recipes, take the timing suggested as a guide only. Learn through experiment what timing works best for your machine.

Advice on Cookpots

I am going to suggest four cookpots that you will find very valuable for both quick cookery, and very low-fat cookery. You don't *have* to have them – in most cases you will probably do very well with what you already have. But if you are just starting out, and wondering how to equip your kitchen, or if you are thinking of updating your equipment, or replacing battered and worn-out items, this brief list may help you decide what to buy.

1   Le Creuset Buffet Casserole. If I had to have one pot, this is the one. The buffet casserole is a 12-inch/30.5-cm wide, 2½-inch/6-cm deep, round, flat-bottomed, enamelled, cast-iron pot with a lid. It works on top of the stove as well as in the oven, and can be used as a frying pan, a casserole, a gratin dish, a baking dish and a saucepan. It comes in a range of colours and is attractive enough to bring to the table, thus eliminating the need to wash an extra serving dish. Enamelled cast iron is sturdy, heavy bottomed, and – if cared for properly – will last for a long time. (Unless you drop it on to a stone floor from a height!)

2   Pyrex or pyroflam 10-inch/25.5-cm square, 2-inch/5-cm deep baking dish with a glass lid. This is another multi-purpose, attractive dish, in this case made from flame-proof ceramic (pyro-ceram). It can go from freezer to oven to table; will work in the microwave as well as on the hob and in the conventional oven; and can be used as a frying pan, baking dish, gratin dish, serving dish and so on.

3   Ridged Grill Pan. A ridged pan goes right on the hob. Heat it (no oil needed), turn on your extractor fan, and you will be able to pan grill pieces of lean meat quickly so that they take on a wonderful, smoky barbecued taste. The ridges leave characteristic grill marks on the meat.

4   Large Non-Stick Wok with Lid. Most cookware shops and department stores sell large woks with flat bottoms, non-stick interiors and lids. The flat bottom enables the wok to sit right on a gas or electric hob, the non-stick interior means that you can cook all sorts of no-fat dishes in it. A wok can be used as a steamer, a frying pan and a saucepan. Tomato sauces can be prepared in your wok, or Therapeutic Vegetable Stews (see pages 88–91) or soups or steamed fish fillets.

Note: All of these are *non-reactive* cookware. Non-reactive means that the pan will not react with acid ingredients (wine, tomatoes and citrus juices, for example) to produce nasty colours and tastes in the finished dish. Non-reactive materials are stainless steel, enamelled cast iron, non-stick coatings such as Tefal and Silverstone, and flame-proof glass and ceramic (pyroflam, pyrex, etc.).

Other Useful Cookware

Non-stick baking trays
A 3½ pint/2 l, 7 inch/18 cm top diameter, opaque white-plastic measuring jug for making microwave sauces, puddings and tortes

Handy Gadgets and Utensils That Make Cooking Easier

Flexible palette knife
Kitchen scissors
Citrus zester
Efficient can opener
Sharp knives (dull knives are dangerous, and will slow you down)
Measuring jugs and spoons
A reliable set of kitchen scales
Brush (for brushing on marinades, milk washes, etc.)
Whisk
Food processor
Blender
A set of American measuring scoops (¼, ⅓, ½ and 1 cup) for making 'Puddle Cakes' (see page 188). They are available in many cookware shops and department stores (see Mail Order Guide, page 191).

Advice on Organization

No matter how busy you are, cooking should never be haphazard. Spontaneity is wonderful – you get an urge for something, and suddenly there you are in the kitchen, cooking up a storm, well on your way to satisfying that urge. But without organization, happy spontaneity is impossible. You know what you and your family like to eat. Plan your shopping trips so that your freezer, store cupboard and fridge are always ready to supply ingredients for those things. Organize your kitchen. Everything should have a place; each piece of equipment, each ingredient should always be in its place. Nothing should slow you down and spoil the fun of the cooking experience, the way frantically searching for something simple (the paring knife, the measuring spoons, the citrus zester, the *salt*!) does.

Keep things in logical places. The salt shaker and pepper grinder belong next to the hob. If you become devoted to the quick bread-baking recipes in the Bread Chapter, keep the flour canister, the honey, the seeds and so on in one place, near the food processor. Then, when you need to bake a fast loaf, you don't have to scurry around like a headless chicken trying to find everything and gather it all together from far-flung corners of the room. If you fall under the spell of the five-minute microwave cakes (see page 187), keep all the utensils needed for the cakes, along with the canisters of dry ingredients, in a single place near the microwave. Have measuring scoops of the proper size already in the canisters of dry ingredients, so you can start scooping, whisking and cooking immediately. A quick recipe does you no good if it takes you longer to gather the ingredients and equipment than it does to cook it.

Clean Up

Cooking is not drudgery. If you are organized and have the proper equipment and a store cupboard, freezer and fridge full of useful ingredients, cooking is creative, calming, satisfying and pleasurable. Setting the table? No problem there. Table setting is another creative activity that is heightened by the fizzing and sizzling sense of anticipation that surrounds it. The kitchen smells wonderful, things are simmering away, soon you'll be *eating*! And the actual dining? Pure pleasure of course. When you are eating food that you love and trust, surrounded by people you love, who love both you and your cooking, life could hardly offer more satisfaction. But clean up? Now, *that's* drudgery. In fact, it's the pits. It's *clean up* that has given cookery a bad name. Show me a food-loving person who hates to cook, and I'll show you an individual who turns faint at the sight of a crumb-strewn floor, a pile of encrusted pots and a ravaged kitchen counter. I can't make the knotty problem of clean up disappear, but I can attempt to make it a little easier for you to deal with.

1   Persuade someone else to do the work. In some households (I've heard rumours about such situations) there is a rule: whoever does the cooking does *not* have to clean up. This rule was invented, I'm sure, by a man who adores cooking but develops severe heart palpitations at the sight of the rubble-strewn kitchen that is the result of his labours. If you are a man, and you promise to do all the shopping, cooking and table setting, maybe the woman with whom you share the house will agree that he who cooks need never clean up. (Don't use it as an excuse, however, to leave the kitchen looking like the aftermath of a severe earthquake.) If you are a woman who shops, cooks and table sets and you share the household with a man, I urge you to unload the cleaning detail on that man. You may have my full blessing. You will, of course, have to give him a few kind and discreet pointers

26

on the nature of dirt and how to control it; women have an ability to find and recognize dirt that goes far beyond that of men. This is not sexism, this is a simple biological fact.

2   If both the male and female heads of the house are unable to come to an equitable understanding about who does the clean up, unload it on to the kids. If you are a single parent, you should definitely unload it on to the kids.

3   Buy a dishwasher. Save your money, even if it takes you years, and you have to economize in other areas. In the course of my cooking life, I've been with a dishwasher, and without one, and believe me, *with* is far better. If you just cook for yourself, a dishwasher may not make that much difference, but if you cook for a houseful, then the blessed machine will be infinitely useful. It's not just that it washes your dishes for you (and gets them really clean), it also keeps chaos at bay. As you use things, as you clean the table, stack things neatly in the machine. Life is so much more pleasant when the dirty dishes are out of sight.

4   Whether or not you have a dishwasher, *clean up as you go*. It's hard to stay sane, efficient and happy when you are surrounded by chaos.

5   There is one exception to clean-up-as-you-go: if the pots and pans you have used are stubbornly encrusted, don't waste time scrubbing them. Soak them overnight in a slurry of biological detergent and water. The next day, they will easily wash clean.

6   Never use 2–3 pots when one will do. Many cookpots will go from fridge to cooker to table, and – if necessary – back to the fridge again. See page 24 for advice on such cookware.

Before You Begin

A Note on Calorie Counts

There is nothing more boring or self-defeating than doggedly counting Calories. It can lead to fear of food, periods of too rigorous dieting interspersed with destructive bingeing and the loss of any culinary enjoyment or spontaneity.

If you follow the Slim Cuisine basics, and cut out the fats and fatty foods listed on pages 13–14, you will never have to resort to the tedium of Calorie counting. If you eliminate the fat, the Calories take care of themselves. Food is meant to be eaten with pleasure, to give us joy, keep us healthy and provide comfort. Obsessively totalling up the Calories contained in everything you eat can spoil all of that.

A Note on Portion Sizes

How many people will a particular recipe serve? What a question! How hungry are you and the people you plan to feed? Are you a nibbler, a gorger or a picker? When (and what) was your last meal or snack? Because I do not have the answers to these vital questions, I am giving you plenty of leeway as far as portion size is concerned. And remember – one of the important points of Slim Cuisine is that large portions are permissible. One person's portion is another person's tantalizing tease and yet another person's over-indulgence. It is Slim Cuisine policy to allow you the freedom to decide for yourself what constitutes a serving according to the occasion and the diners. That is why, whenever possible, the yield is given in volume (for instance, 1½ pts) or in pieces (4 chicken thighs). Because the fat density is so dramatically diminished, and Calorie counting is eliminated, portion control is no longer strictly necessary.

How To Tackle a Recipe

If you are organized, you will be efficient when you cook, and you won't waste precious time. The rules are simple.

1 First read the recipe through completely.

2 Preheat the oven or grill, put the water on to boil, start things going in a logical way.

3 Don't waste time. While the first part of a recipe is simmering or roasting, chop, slice and measure whatever is necessary for the next few steps.

4 All ingredients are given in imperial and in metric measurements. Use one or the other, but do not mix measurements in any one recipe.

RECIPE SYMBOLS

Therapeutic Binge: There is no limit to a therapeutic binge recipe – eat all you want, as often as you like. TBs will keep you full, happy, slim and healthy. Depend on them – they feed that bottomless hunger without expanding the bottom.

A recipe with a heart is *very* low in both fat and sugar. Not quite a therapeutic binge, but still suitable for weight loss. (A recipe without a 🐻, or without a ♡, is suitable for weight maintenance.)

🍶 Any recipe that carries this symbol is suitable for vegetarians.

❄ Snowflaked recipes can be frozen.

🥫 A can represents a store-cupboard recipe. Such a recipe can be put together almost entirely from store-cupboard staples.

⊠ This symbol indicates that a microwave is needed to prepare this recipe.

🕐 For each recipe, an *approximate* time of preparation is given. I stress the word *approximate*, because every cook has his or her own speed and efficiency (or lack of speed and efficiency!). The estimated time is meant to cover the entire recipe from peeling, chopping and dicing ingredients, through to actual cooking time.

Weight Loss Note

If you want to *lose* weight only eat 🐻 and ♡ recipes. If you want to lose weight *quickly*, eat 🐻 recipes, augmented with skimmed milk dairy products (see list, page 14). (Some of the maintenance recipes are followed by suggestions to modify them to ♡ [weight loss] or 🐻 [therapeutic binge].)

If you wish to *maintain* your weight, eat freely from all the recipes in this book. You may, however, find that you are eating freely from the recipes in the book, and still slowly losing weight. If you want to stop losing weight, and simply maintain a specific weight, just eat more.

Soups

Some soups are glorious eaten on their own. All that's needed to round out a hearty soup meal is some bread with character and an inspiring dessert. (Let's face it; an inspiring dessert is necessary to round out any meal properly. But that's another chapter.) If you keep the freezer well supplied with frozen vegetables and stock, the store cupboard full of potatoes, garlic, tomato juice and canned tomatoes, beans and sweetcorn; and the fridge stocked with spring onions and fresh herbs, then you always have a wealth of soup possibilities for main dishes and first courses, family dining and dinner parties. Soup is both filling and comforting. For those of us who only feel well fed if their evening meal is substantial, soup is the perfect beginning. Use these recipes as guides – their principles should direct you towards your own personal style.

 PURÉE OF PEA SOUP

Yields 2¾ pts/1.6 l

⏱ 12–15 minutes

This is a soup made with *frozen* peas and skimmed milk, yet it tastes garden fresh and indulgently creamy. Augmenting the

31

skimmed milk with skimmed milk powder gives it a deep creaminess (because the fat content is virtually nil, it is *creamy* without being *cloying*), and brief cooking ensures that the peas keep their vibrant colour and fresh taste. Simple and quick though it is, the soup is very elegant, and could easily be a dinner party staple as well as a family favourite.

12 spring onions, trimmed and sliced	½ pt/300 ml skimmed milk mixed with 3 tablespoons skimmed milk powder
1½ pts/900 ml stock	
20 oz/550 g frozen green peas	
2–3 tablespoons shredded fresh mint	Salt and freshly ground pepper to taste

1   Combine the onions, ½ pt/300ml stock and the peas in a pot. Simmer until the peas are tender. It will take just a few minutes. Don't overcook them; they should retain their lovely green colour. Purée in small batches in the blender and return to the pot.

2   Stir in the mint and remaining stock. Simmer for 5 minutes. Add the milk. Simmer for 2–3 minutes more. Season to taste.

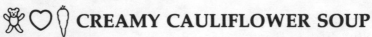 CREAMY CAULIFLOWER SOUP

Yields 2 pts/1.1 l

⊕ 15 minutes

Frozen cauliflower, when cooked, is inferior to cooked fresh cauliflower in texture, but it is exquisite in a puréed soup, when texture doesn't matter but flavour does. This lovely cream soup is perfumed with tarragon and a hint of allspice.

12 spring onions, trimmed and sliced	⅛ teaspoon ground allspice
	1½ pts/900 ml stock
20 oz/550 g frozen cauliflower florets	½ pt/300 ml skimmed milk mixed with 3 tablespoons skimmed milk powder
½ teaspoon dried tarragon	
Pinch or two ground cayenne pepper	Salt and freshly ground pepper to taste

1   Combine the onions, cauliflower, tarragon, cayenne pepper, allspice and ½ pt/300 ml stock in a pot. Simmer until the cauliflower is tender. Purée in small batches in the blender and return to the pot.

2   Stir in the remaining stock. Simmer for 5 minutes. Add the milk. Simmer a further 2–3 minutes. Season to taste.

SPICY CORN SOUP

Yields approx 2 pts/1.1 l

🕐 15–20 minutes

Many supermarkets now carry frozen sweetcorn that has been bred to be extra sweet. If you can find such corn, use it here. This soup glows with colour, sweetcorn flavour and a hint of underlying spiciness.

---

12 spring onions, trimmed and
   sliced
20 oz/550 g frozen sweetcorn
⅛ teaspoon ground cumin
⅛ teaspoon ground coriander
Pinch ground cayenne pepper (to
   taste)
1½ pts/900 ml stock
2–3 tablespoons chopped mixed
   fresh herbs (chives, oregano and

coriander)
½ pt/300 ml skimmed milk mixed
   with 3 tablespoons skimmed
   milk powder
Salt and freshly ground pepper to
   taste
Garnish: approximately 4 oz/110 g
   cooked sweetcorn and 1–2
   tablespoons snipped chives

---

1   Combine the onions, sweetcorn, cumin, coriander, cayenne pepper and ½ pt/300 ml stock in a pot. Simmer until the corn is tender. Purée in small batches in a blender and return to the pot.
2   Stir in the herbs and the remaining stock. Simmer for 5 minutes. Add the milk. Simmer for 2–3 minutes more. Season to taste. Garnish with some of the cooked sweetcorn and a pinch of snipped chives.

❄ SMOKY POTATO–CHICK PEA SOUP

Yields 3 pts/1.7 l

🕐 Approx ½ hour

A huge bowl of steaming soup filled with meat, potatoes and chick peas, accompanied by a crusty loaf of freshly baked bread makes a splendid meal at the end of a long and miserable day. This is the kind of hearty soup that takes minutes to make, but tastes as if it has simmered for considerably longer. For the fresh-baked loaf, see page 141.

2 rashers smoked back bacon, trimmed of all fat	2 baking potatoes, peeled and cut in chunks
6–7 sun-dried tomatoes, snipped with scissors	1 piece Parmesan rind – optional
1 pinch dried chilli peppers	14 oz/400 g can chick peas, drained
1 fresh chilli, chopped	Salt and freshly ground pepper to taste
2 onions, chopped	2 tablespoons freshly chopped parsley
4 cloves garlic, crushed	
2½ pts/1.4 l stock	2 tablespoons freshly chopped basil
4 fl oz/110 ml dry white vermouth	

1   In a heavy bottomed soup pot, combine the bacon, sun-dried tomatoes, dried chilli peppers, fresh chilli, onions, garlic, ½ pt/300 ml stock and dry white vermouth. Cover and boil for 5–7 minutes. Uncover and simmer briskly until the onions are tender and browned, and the liquid is almost gone.

2   Add the potatoes, Parmesan rind if using, and remaining 2 pts/1.1 l stock. Simmer partially covered until the potatoes are tender (approx 10–15 minutes).

3   Lightly crush a few of the potato pieces against the side of the pot with a wooden spoon. Add the chick peas and season to taste. Cook for another 3–4 minutes to heat through. Stir in the parsley and basil.

♡   Omit bacon.

♡   **PRAWN NOODLE SOUP**

Yields 2½ pts/1.4 l

⏲ Approx 25 minutes

Here is a most satisfying bowl of noodle soup, spiked with Thai flavourings: chilli peppers, garlic, ginger, lime and lemon grass. Many supermarkets now stock lemon grass; it looks like a fibrous, tough, thin spring onion. If you can't find it, don't worry. If you leave it out, the recipe will still make a lovely bowl of soup.

12 spring onions, cleaned and trimmed	3 pts/1.7 l stock
	Several dashes Teriyaki sauce
1–2 chilli peppers, minced	8 oz/225 g vermicelli or angel-hair pasta (very thin spaghetti)
3 cloves garlic, crushed	
1 teaspoon grated fresh ginger	1 stalk lemon grass – optional
Grated rind and juice of 1 lime	8 oz/225 g tiny cooked, peeled prawns
Handful fresh coriander	

1   Slice the bulb portion of the spring onions, then chop the greens and save them for later. Combine the white portions with the chillies, garlic, ginger, grated rind and juice of *half* the lime, chopped *stems* (save the remainder for later) of the coriander, ½ pt/300 ml stock and Teriyaki sauce in a heavy, non-reactive pot. Cover and boil for 7–10 minutes. Uncover and simmer briskly until the garlic and onions are 'frying' in the syrupy juices.

2   When the garlic is tender, stir in all the remaining ingredients (including the outstanding stock, lime juice and rind) *except* the prawns. Simmer uncovered, stirring occasionally, until the noodles are tender. Take out the stalk of lemon grass. Remove from the heat and stir in the prawns, chopped coriander leaves and sliced spring onion greens. Stir for a moment or two to heat through and then serve.

BARBECUED PORK, NOODLE SOUP

Yields 2½ pts/1.4 l

🕐 ½ hour (Roast the pork and prepare the soup at the same time.)

Another bowl of noodles, this time Chinese style, topped with slices of Chinese Barbecued Pork. This is a lean version of the kind of noodle soup you get from the noodle cart that trundles around the tables at old-fashioned Chinese Dim Sum restaurants. It is – obviously – a meal in itself.

---

12 spring onions, cleaned and trimmed	*Several dashes Teriyaki sauce*
1–2 chilli peppers, minced	*8 oz/225 g vermicelli (very thin spaghetti)*
3 cloves garlic, crushed	*1 recipe Barbecued Pork Tenderloin, Chinese Style, (see page 55)*
1 teaspoon grated fresh ginger	
Handful fresh coriander	
3 pts/1.7 l stock	

---

1 Slice the bulb portion of the spring onions, then chop the greens and save them for later. Combine the white portions with the chillies, garlic, ginger, sliced *stems* (save the remainder for later) of the coriander, ½ pint/300 ml stock and Teriyaki sauce in a heavy, non-reactive pot. Cover and boil for 7–10 minutes. Uncover and simmer briskly until the garlic and onions are 'frying' in the syrupy juices.

2 When the garlic is tender, stir in all the remaining ingredients (including the outstanding stock) *except* the pork. Simmer uncovered, stirring occasionally, until the noodles are tender. Stir in a tablespoon or so of the marinade from the bottom of the pork baking pan. Add the coriander and sliced spring onion greens. Stir for a moment or two to heat through. Serve with a generous portion of sliced pork heaped on top of each bowlful.

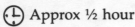 **CORN CHOWDER**

Yields 3¼ pts/1.8 l

⊕ Approx ½ hour

Fresh sweetcorn is at its best plucked from its stalk, rushed to the cooker on which a pot of boiling water waits, plunged in, boiled briefly and devoured. Need I say that under ordinary circumstances this is not practical? It's fortunate that frozen sweetcorn is such an excellent product. Look for bags of frozen sweetcorn that indicate that it has been bred for extra sweetness.

12 spring onions, trimmed and sliced	1 yellow pepper, peeled and coarsely diced
2 well-trimmed slices smoked back bacon, diced	8 oz/225 g all-purpose (Maris Piper) potatoes, cut into ½-inch/1 cm cubes
1–2 cloves garlic, minced	
2 pts/1.1 l stock	Salt and freshly ground pepper to taste
Several pinches dried tarragon	
Cayenne pepper to taste	1 lb/450 g bag frozen sweetcorn kernels
2 fl oz/50 ml dry vermouth	
4 oz/110 g button mushrooms, quartered	8 fl oz/225 ml skimmed milk mixed with 2 tablespoons dried skimmed milk powder
Dash or two Teriyaki sauce	
1 red pepper, peeled and coarsely diced	2–3 tablespoons chopped parsley

1   Combine the onions, bacon, garlic, 5 fl oz/150 ml stock, tar-
    ragon, cayenne pepper and vermouth in a soup pot. Cook
    together until the onions and garlic are tender, and the liquid
    is almost gone.
2   Add the mushrooms, Teriyaki sauce and a further 5 fl oz/
    150 ml stock. Cook gently for a few minutes until the
    mushrooms are beginning to get tender and have exuded
    quite a bit of liquid. Stir in the peppers and cook for 2–3
    minutes more.
3   Stir in the potatoes and add some salt and pepper to taste.
    Pour in the remaining stock. Simmer, partially covered, until
    the potatoes are almost tender. Add the corn. Simmer,
    partially covered, until both the corn and potatoes are soft.
4   Mix together the milk and milk powder, then add gradually,
    while stirring, to the soup. Simmer for 5 minutes. Taste and
    adjust seasonings.
5   Purée 2 ladlefuls of the soup in a blender, 1 ladleful at a time.
    (Hold down the cover and avert your face.) Combine blended
    and unblended portions. Stir in the parsley. Serve piping
    hot.

♡   Omit bacon.

♡   **FISH SOUP**

Yields approx 2 pts/1.1 l

⏲ Approx 25 minutes

Except for the spring onions and parsley, this soup is put together
from the store cupboard and freezer, and can be completed in less
than half an hour. What's more, it is cooked in (and served from)
just one pot. And oh yes – it is quite delicious. The flavour base
consists of vermouth, fennel, garlic, chillies and a few diced, sun-
dried tomatoes. Some supermarkets carry excellent fish stock in
their chill cabinet, otherwise you can use vegetable stock or even
chicken stock.

6 spring onions, trimmed and sliced	1 pt/570 ml tomato juice
4 fl oz/110 ml white vermouth	1 bay leaf
1½ pts/900 ml stock	Salt and freshly ground pepper to
½ teaspoon fennel seeds	taste
Pinch dried crushed chillies	1 lb/450 g skinless frozen white fish
2 cloves crushed garlic	fillets
3–4 sun-dried tomatoes, diced –	Chopped fresh parsley for garnish
optional	

1   Combine the onions, vermouth, ½ pt/300 ml stock, fennel seeds, chillies, garlic and sun-dried tomatoes in a flame-proof casserole. Cover and boil for 7 minutes. Uncover and simmer briskly until the liquid is almost gone, and the garlic is tender.
2   Add all the remaining ingredients (including the outstanding stock) *except* the fish and garnish. Simmer uncovered for 10 minutes.
3   Add the fish and simmer covered for 5–7 minutes or until the fish is just done. Discard the bay leaf. Break up the fish pieces with a serving spoon. Ladle the fish and broth into soup bowls, and sprinkle each serving with some chopped parsley.

TOMATO SORBET

Yields ½ pt/300 ml

⏱5 minutes (have the tomatoes ready frozen – see note below)

Not long ago, I went through a savoury vegetable sorbet phase – my loyal tasters sat through cabbage sorbet, green-pea sorbet, beetroot sorbet, even Brussels-sprout sorbet. All through the tasting, as I madly threw even stranger frozen vegetables into the food processor, they smiled bravely and remained calm, which is why I love them so much. But I could tell by the light in their eyes that they thought I had finally totally flipped, and probably needed a long rest in a quiet place. But the Tomato Sorbet: oh! it was delicious. We all agreed that it was a frosty, vibrant and spicy winner. Imagine, on a hot summer's evening, sitting down to a crystal goblet of Bloody Mary Soup (recipe follows) in which a scoop of this sorbet nestles. Gorgeous – that's what it is!

---

8 oz/225 g (1 14 oz/400 g tin)
    frozen tomatoes (see note)
Juice of ½ lime
3 tablespoons shredded fresh basil or

mint
Several dashes Worcestershire and
    Tabasco sauce

---

1   Put all the ingredients into the container of a food processor.
2   Process, stopping to scrape down the sides as necessary, until the mixture forms an icy sorbet consistency. With an ice-cream scoop, scoop the icy mixture into balls and serve at once.
Note: To freeze tomatoes, drain canned tomatoes very well. (Save the juice for recipes such as Bloody Mary Soup [see page 39] or Fish Soup [see page 37].) Halve the tomatoes. Spread the tomatoes out in one layer on a non-stick baking tray and freeze solid. When frozen, gather into a bag, seal and store in the freezer until needed.

BLOODY MARY SOUP

Yields 1¾ pts/1 l

⏲ 5 minutes

In the early seventies, I was in charge of the kitchen of a small bistro-type restaurant in Atlanta, Georgia. Sunday brunch was one of our specialities. The restaurant was housed in an old and charming cottage on a tree-lined street, and on Sundays, folks would come early, dressed in casual clothes and laden with the Sunday papers. They would settle on the shady front porch for a leisurely morning of relaxed eating and socializing. My problem was that everyone wanted a Bloody Mary on Sunday morning to help wash down their bagels, waffles and omelettes. In those days, it was illegal to serve alcoholic drinks before noon on a Sunday, but my customers would begin to arrive at 10.00 a.m., craving food and *drink*. Oddly enough, although it was illegal to serve alcohol in glasses, there was no law against lacing *food* liberally with alcohol at any time of any day or night, so I took to serving Bloody Mary Soup in large soup plates, with nice big spoons and the admonition to spoon it up decorously. I don't think that there has ever been such a popular soup in the history of soup-making. In the summer time, I still make that soup often, but without the vodka or gin, which I've always hated anyway. A gobletful, with a scoop of Tomato Sorbet in the centre, and a few sprigs of basil or mint, is a splendid beginning to an alfresco Sunday summer brunch or lunch.

---

1 box (1¾ pts/1 l) chilled tomato juice	*Juice of ½ lime*
Several dashes Tabasco sauce (to taste)	*A dash or two celery salt – optional*
	Tomato Sorbet (page 38)
1 teaspoon Worcestershire sauce	*Mint or basil leaves for garnish*

---

1   Combine all the ingredients except the sorbet and garnish.
2   Serve in clear glass goblets or soup plates. Centre a scoop of tomato sorbet (see previous recipe) in each serving. Garnish with a mint or basil leaf.

Variation:

 **COLD TOMATO-ORANGE SOUP**

Yields 1¾ pts/1 l

⏰ 5 minutes

---

1 box (1¾ pts/1 l) chilled tomato
   juice
2 tablespoons frozen orange juice
   concentrate, thawed

1 teaspoon sugar
Several dashes each: Worcestershire
   and Tabasco sauce

Whisk all the ingredients together. Serve in soup plates or clear glass goblets with a scoop of tomato sorbet in each serving.

Dips, Spreads and Pâtés

In the very early sixties when I was beginning to cook, there was a newly developing concept in the air called 'chip 'n dip'. Everything about it was awful: the horrible ' 'n' between 'chip' and 'dip'; the greasy, salty, packaged chips themselves; and the dips – usually canned clams or dehydrated onion soup mixed with gum-laden cream cheese. I shudder with revulsion just thinking about it. Don't let the memory of such abominations turn you off dips. Some of the most classic of preparations are dips of sorts: think of hummus, aioli, bagna cauda, cheese fondue, chopped liver . . . respectable (but fattening!) dips appear in all cultures.

With the help of a food processor and a well-stocked store cupboard and freezer, all sorts of splendid, rich-tasting, *low-fat* dips can be made in a snap. Spread these mixtures on toast, dip them up with vegetable crudités, dollop them into button-mushroom caps and chicory leaves and gobble them up for starters, between-meals snacks or midnight comforts. Many of them make great sandwich fillings too.

TUNA PÂTÉ WITH LEMON CHUTNEY

Yields ½ pt/300 ml

⏱ 5 minutes

If you keep jars of interesting chutneys and pickles, and tins of water-packed tuna in your store cupboard you can – with the addition of some quark – make the most amazing instant Tuna Pâté. The pâté can be spread on toast quarters, or on matzo crackers, and would not be out of place as a first course for a really elegant dinner. The recipe can easily be doubled, if necessary.

1 can (7 oz/200 g) tuna in water or brine, well drained	chutney or lime-chilli pickle
4–5 tablespoons Tuscan lemon	2–3 oz/50–75 g quark or skimmed milk curd cheese

1 Place all the ingredients in the container of a food processor. Blend until the mixture is well combined and smooth.
2 Serve as a sandwich filling, a spread or a dip.

 # MUSHROOM-APPLE PÂTÉ

Yields 1¾ pts/1 l

⏱ Approx 15 minutes

This makes a dark, luscious-textured, rich-tasting pâté that is delicious spread thickly on to toast or savoury biscuits. If you can find shiitake mushrooms and chestnut (brown-caps) mushrooms, use a few – along with the usual cultivated ones – to provide an even richer taste and darker colour.

3 oz/75 g dried apple rings, cut into pieces	2–3 cloves garlic, minced
8 fl oz/225 ml dry sherry	4 fl oz/110 ml stock
4 fl oz/110 ml water	Dash or two Teriyaki sauce
2 lbs/900 g mushrooms, washed and sliced	1 teaspoon ground coriander
	Pinch or two cayenne pepper
	Salt and freshly ground pepper

1 Soak the apple pieces in 4 fl oz/110 ml sherry and 4 fl oz/ 110 ml water.
2 Meanwhile, combine the mushrooms, garlic, stock, remaining sherry and Teriyaki sauce in a non-reactive, heavy frying pan. Simmer briskly, stirring occasionally. When the liquid is almost gone, add the apples and their liquid, the coriander

and cayenne pepper. Simmer, stirring occasionally until all the liquid has gone. Season with salt and pepper.

3   Place the mushroom mixture in a food processor and blend until smooth. Mound the mixture in a bowl, cover and refrigerate until needed.

SPINACH DIP

Yields approx 1 pt/570 ml

Approx 15 minutes

Why has spinach had such a bad press? It tastes so good, it looks so green and inviting, it's so *versatile*. Maybe it was that old *New Yorker* cartoon that started the bad spinach vibes: a bratty kid looks at the plate of green vegetables his mother has set before him and snarls, 'I says it's spinach, and I say the hell with it!' All the Popeye cartoons in the world seem unable to undo that one, now classic, spinach attack. Of course, Popeye gulped it out of a can, and canned spinach is awful. Fortunately, it freezes beautifully, so fast foodies don't even have to think about touching the canned stuff. This fresh green dip, based on frozen spinach, works well with raw vegetables or spread on crackers.

7 spring onions, trimmed and sliced	*½ pint/300 ml stock*
3 cloves garlic	*10 oz/275 g frozen chopped spinach*
2–3 sun-dried tomatoes, snipped	*½ small carton (3½ oz/85 g) quark*
(use scissors)	*or skimmed milk curd cheese*
Pinch or two nutmeg	*3 tablespoons Parmesan cheese*
Pinch or two cayenne pepper	

1   In a heavy bottomed frying pan, combine the onions, garlic, sun-dried tomatoes, nutmeg, cayenne pepper and stock. Cover and boil for 7–10 minutes. Uncover and simmer until the garlic is tender and the liquid has almost gone.

2   Meanwhile, thaw the spinach in the microwave. Put it in a colander, and – with your hands – squeeze it as dry as possible.

3   Combine the spinach, garlic mixture, quark and Parmesan cheese in a food processor. Blend until smooth. Mound the mixture in a bowl, cover and refrigerate until needed.

 Omit Parmesan cheese.

♡ ⦶ GREEN PEA DIP (MOCK GUACAMOLE)

Yields 1 pt/570 ml

🕐 Approx 5 minutes

I'm repeating this here from *Slim Cuisine: A Second Helping*, because it is fast, fresh and wonderful to eat. Real guacamole, of course, is made with avocado, but avocado has a staggeringly high fat content. The texture of the peas doesn't really mimic the texture of avocado, but the purée is good enough to stand on its own merit. Not only is this pea purée good as a dip or spread; it also works as a garnish for Mexican Grilled Beef (see page 51).

3–4 tablespoons fresh coriander leaves	(defrost in the microwave if necessary)
2 tablespoons lime juice	¼ teaspoon ground cumin
1 fresh chilli pepper, seeded and coarsely diced	Salt to taste
1 lb/450 g defrosted frozen peas	3–4 spring onions, trimmed and diced

1 Place the coriander, lime juice and chilli in the jar of a food processor. Blend until coarsely chopped.
2 Add the peas, cumin and salt and process to a rough purée. Scrape into a bowl and stir in the onion. Serve with toasted split pitta-bread wedges or matzo crackers.

♡ ⦶ ❄ ⧠ CANNELLINI-RED PEPPER DIP

Yields 1 pt/570 ml

🕐 Approx 10 minutes

This dip is a spicy, rosy-coloured, texturally delightful, store-cupboard gem. I *love* it, as you can plainly deduce. Conceptually, it is a relative of hummus, that classic dip of chick peas and sesame seeds; here cannellini beans and cumin seeds are used instead. The cumin seeds are simmered in stock with garlic, chilli flakes and sun-dried tomatoes to make a flavour base for the purée.

1 can (15¾ oz/430 g) cannellini beans	¼ teaspoon cumin seeds
1 can (15¾ oz/430 g) red peppers (pimientos)	4–5 sun-dried tomatoes, diced (use scissors) – optional
3 cloves garlic, crushed	½ pt/300 ml stock
Good pinch dried chilli flakes	Salt and freshly ground pepper to taste

1   Empty the beans and the peppers into a colander. Rinse under cold water and set aside to drain well.
2   Combine the garlic, chillies, cumin seeds, tomatoes if using and stock in a non-reactive frying pan. Cover and boil for 3–4 minutes. Uncover and simmer until the garlic is tender and the liquid has cooked down considerably and become syrupy.
3   Combine the drained beans and peppers in a food processor container. Add the garlic-chilli infusion. Season with salt and pepper. Blend to a rough purée. Scrape into a bowl and refrigerate until needed.

CURRIED APRICOT SPREAD

Yields 8 fl oz/225 ml

 Approx 5 minutes

Use this spicy sandwich spread on smoked turkey-watercress sandwiches or cucumber sandwiches, or sliced beetroot-raw spinach leaf sandwiches. The spread also works well as a dip for raw vegetables, especially peppery ones such as radishes or sticks of white turnip.

1½ tablespoons low-sugar apricot jam	1 small carton (7 oz/200 g) quark or skimmed milk curd cheese
½ teaspoon Garam Masala	

---

1   Stir together the jam and the Garam Masala.
2   Put it into a processor with the quark. Blend until smooth and well combined. (Alternatively whisk together in a large bowl.) Scrape into a small bowl, cover and refrigerate until needed.

CREAMY HERB SPREAD

Yields ¾ pt/400 ml

Approx 5 minutes

Use this sweet-and-sour, herb-flecked, creamy mixture as a sandwich spread or – thinned with additional buttermilk or milk – as a salad dressing. It's especially good for salads that contain both sweet and savoury components: red onion and oranges, for instance, or sliced fennel, mandarin sections and sliced chicory. The spread also makes a good dip for raw vegetables.

2 cartons (7½ oz/210 g each) quark
  or no-fat curd cheese
4 tablespoons buttermilk or fromage
  frais
1½ tablespoons runny mild honey
1 tablespoon Balsamic vinegar
½ teaspoon Worcestershire sauce
Several dashes Tabasco sauce

1 clove garlic, crushed – optional
4–6 tablespoons mixed chopped
  herbs (parsley, chives, basil and
  thyme; or parsley, chives, mint
  and coriander; or parsley,
  chives, dill and marjoram)
Freshly ground pepper to taste

1   Whirl all the ingredients in a food processor until fluffy and
    flecked with green. Refrigerate until needed.

Meat, Poultry and Fish

Often, when people hear that I write books about healthy eating, they announce, smugly: 'I never eat red meat, you know', as if they immediately should be awarded the gold medal for healthy living. Don't fall for the popular myth that meat is unhealthy. *Fatty* meat is certainly to be avoided, and huge daily servings of meat are totally unnecessary, but reasonable portions (4–5 oz/110–150 g) 2–3 times a week can only improve your nutritional profile. Meat contains an impressive package of vitamins, minerals and trace minerals; in fact animal products are the *only* dietary source of vitamin B^{12}, and the iron and zinc in meat comes in the form that is most easily absorbed by the human body.

Here are cuts of *very lean* meat to slot into your weekly menus; not only are they extremely good tasting and nutritionally important, they can be cooked *very* quickly.

1   Extra lean mince – pork, beef, veal or lamb. The best way to ensure leanness in mince is to choose a piece of extra lean meat from a trusted butcher and have him mince it. The recipes in this chapter that call for lean mince add various ingredients to mince that impart good texture (if not properly handled, lean mince can be pebbly and dry) and stretch it so that a large satisfying portion of a particular recipe contains only a modest serving of meat.

2   Goose Skirt (sometimes called Flank Skirt) Steak (Americans call it 'Flank steak'). A very lean, flat, paddle-shaped cut of beef, usually about 1–1½ lbs/450–700 g in weight. A goose skirt is easily trimmed of its small amount of surrounding fat. (The butcher may consent to do it for you, but he also may complain bitterly that removal of every vestige of fat will mar the quality of the meat. Ignore his complaints.) Goose skirt cooks very quickly indeed and makes an incredibly juicy, deeply flavoured piece of meat. A ridged grill pan (see page 24) is ideal for indoor, stove-top grilling, but the meat can also be grilled under the grill in your cooker, or on a barbecue.

3   Pork tenderloin (also called pork fillet). Pork is bred to be very lean these days, therefore most traditional pork recipes conceived when pork was fattier don't work any more: the cooking times are too long and the finished meat emerges woefully tough and overcooked. Pork tenderloin gives very good value – only a modest amount of surrounding fat needs to be trimmed away before the meat is ready for cooking. A pork tenderloin cooks to juicy perfection in a very hot oven in less than half an hour.

4   Pork loin. Another lean cut of pork: for quick cooking look for boneless pork loin steaks in the supermarket. They need to be trimmed of their thin rim of fat and then they are ready to be quickly grilled (or pan-fried in a non-stick frying pan).

❄   **MEXICAN SHEPHERD'S PIE**

Meat mixture yields 2 pts/1.1 l
Potato-Polenta yields 2½ pts/1.4 l

🕐 Approx 40 minutes

I love Shepherd's Pie, but until I moved to England eight years ago, I had never encountered one. It took a transatlantic move to introduce me to the gorgeously meaty, potato-blanketed pie. Basic recipes like Shepherd's Pie are such fun. What wonderful scope they give for improvization and variation. For this variation, minced pork simmers briefly with lentils and Mexican seasoning and then is blanketed with a quickly made topping of polenta mixed with mashed potatoes. (If you have no polenta, mashed potatoes on their own are just fine.) Finally, it is grilled till it browns. In my opinion, family food doesn't get much better than this.

1 lb/450 g very lean ground pork	1 clove garlic, crushed
1 tablespoon chilli powder	4 oz/110 g tiny orange lentils
1 teaspoon crumbled dried oregano	1 pt/570 ml stock
¼ teaspoon ground cinnamon	4 fl oz/110 ml tomato passata
½ teaspoon ground cumin	Salt and freshly ground pepper to
½ teaspoon crushed chillies	taste
1 large onion, peeled and chopped fine	Potato-Polenta topping (see page 17)
2 carrots, peeled and chopped fine	2 tablespoons skimmed milk
1 red pepper, peeled, seeded and chopped	3 tablespoons grated Parmesan cheese

1   Combine the pork, spices, onion, carrots, pepper and garlic in a heavy pan. If possible, use one that can go into the oven as well as on the stove top, like a Le Creuset buffet casserole or a Corning Ware 10 inch/25.5 cm square, 2-inch/5-cm deep casserole. Cook, stirring occasionally, breaking up the lumps of meat with a wooden spoon until the meat is done and the vegetables are starting to get softer. Drain the meat into a colander over a bowl. Line the frying pan with paper towels to blot up the fat. Dump in the meat. Use the towel overhang to blot the meat. Slip out the paper towels and discard.

2   Stir in the lentils, stock, tomato passata, salt and pepper. Simmer uncovered for half an hour, or until the mixture is thick, and the lentils are tender. While the mixture cooks, prepare the Potato-Polenta topping and preheat the grill.

3   If you have used an oven-proof pan, spread the meat mixture out evenly; otherwise, spoon the mixture evenly into a gratin dish. Cover with the freshly made Potato-Polenta topping. Sprinkle over the milk and cheese. Grill for 4–5 minutes, until nicely browned.

Note: If you wish, before baking, divide the pie into two or more smaller gratin dishes so that you can make several pies from this recipe: eat one and freeze the others.

MEAT PIE

Meat mixture yields 2pts/1.1 l
Meat pie yields 4 generous squares

⏱ Approx 40 minutes

When my tasters, testers and helpers grab copies of the recipe for a new dish we have just tried, and head upstairs to the photocopier, I know that I have a winner. This down-to-earth, family-style meaty pie caused just such a flurry. It is topped with ready-to-bake baguette dough (available in cylinders in the chill cabinet of many supermarkets) and baked. The meat mixture takes about half an hour to cook, the final baking, 10–12 minutes.

1 lb/450 g very lean minced beef, pork or veal, or a combination	2 fl oz/50 ml dry vermouth
1 onion, peeled and chopped	4 oz/110 g tiny orange lentils
1 carrot, chopped	Salt and freshly ground pepper to taste
1 clove garlic, crushed	1 tablespoon tomato purée
1 pt/570 ml stock	1 tablespoon parsley
Cayenne pepper to taste	2 cylinders ready-to-bake baguettes (see page 163)
2 good pinches dried tarragon	
4 fl oz/110 ml tomato passata	2–3 tablespoons skimmed milk

1   Preheat the oven to 400°F, 200°C, Gas Mark 6.
2   Combine the meat, onion, carrot and garlic in a heavy pan. If possible, use one that can go into the oven as well as on the stove top, like a Le Creuset buffet casserole or a pyroflam or pyrex shallow square casserole. Cook, stirring occasionally, breaking up the lumps of meat with a wooden spoon, until the meat is done and the vegetables are beginning to soften. Drain the meat into a colander over a bowl. Line the frying pan with paper towels to blot up the fat. Dump in the meat. Use the towel overhang to blot the meat. Slip out the paper towels and discard.
3   Stir in the stock, cayenne pepper, tarragon, tomato passata, vermouth, lentils and salt and pepper to taste. Simmer, uncovered, for approximately half an hour, or until the mixture is thick, and the lentils are tender. Add the tomato purée and parsley and simmer very gently for 5 more minutes.
4   If you have used an oven-proof dish, spread the meat mixture out evenly; otherwise, spoon the mixture evenly into a gratin dish.
5   Open the tubes of baguette dough, and unroll it. Lay the dough strips over the meat, and brush them with the milk. Bake uncovered for approximately 12 minutes, or until the bread topping has risen and browned.

Note: If you have no baguette dough, a well-seasoned mashed potato topping works beautifully.

MEXICAN GRILLED BEEF (FAJITAS)

Serves 4

⏱ Approx 25 minutes

Fajitas (pronounced Fa *hee* tas) are strips of grilled (often char-grilled) beef, pork, chicken or goat, served wrapped in wheat tortillas and garnished with hot tomato-chilli salsa, guacamole and sour cream (fromage frais is a perfect substitute for the sour cream). Wheat tortillas are not easily obtained. Even if they were, I wouldn't recommend using them because they contain oil or – more authentically – lard. Instead, wrap your fajitas in pitta bread. Pitta is fat-free, good-quality bread and makes a perfect wrap for the strips of meat and their accompaniments. Of course, using Middle Eastern pitta bread to wrap Mexican grilled beef ruins the ethnic purity of the recipe, but what the hell! I've already ruined its purity by omitting the lard and oil that drenches 'real' Mexican (and Tex-Mex) cookery. So, forget ethnic purity and enjoy – the whole combination makes an exhilarating and fun meal.

---

2 teaspoons brown sugar
1 teaspoon paprika
1 teaspoon ground cumin
1 teaspoon ground coriander
⅛ teaspoon cayenne pepper
Freshly ground black pepper to taste
1 well-trimmed goose skirt steak
   (approx 1 lb/450 g)

Juice of 2 large oranges and 1 lime,
   combined
1–3 cloves garlic, crushed
Garnishes: chopped fresh coriander,
   no-fat fromage frais, Mock
   Guacamole (see page 44), Salsa
   (see page 130)

---

1   Combine the sugar and spices, then rub this mix into both sides of the goose skirt. Pour the juices into a non-reactive baking dish. Add the garlic.

2   Turn the meat in the mixture and let it marinate until you are ready to cook it.

3   Heat a ridged grill pan until hot. (Or, you could grill this on the outdoor barbecue.) With tongs, pull the meat out of the baking dish. Blot the meat on paper towels to dry it, but do *not* rub off the spice mix. Save the marinade juices. Sear the meat on both sides (about 1½ minutes on each side), using tongs to turn it.

4   With a small basting brush, brush the top of the steak with the citrus-juice marinade. Turn and cook (brushing the top side each time you turn the meat) for another 3–5 minutes on each side. It is *medium-rare* when it feels springy – not mushy

– when poked in the centre with your finger. Transfer to a carving board and allow to rest for 3–5 minutes.

5   Carve in thin slices, slightly on the diagonal, against the grain. Put the slices on a platter and pour over them any juices that have accumulated on the board. To serve, have a platter of pitta bread on the table, along with bowls of the garnishes. To eat, fill your pitta with strips of meat topped with salsa, coriander, guacamole and a dollop of fromage frais. To make it perfect, serve Mexican-style baked beans on the side (see page 107). Oh, what deliciously messy *fun* this meal is to eat!

Cook until done

To test if a piece of grilled meat is done to your liking, poke it with your finger. If it feels *mushy*, it is very rare. If it is *springy*, it is medium-rare. If it is *firm*, it is well done.

THAI-STYLE BEEF SALAD

Serves 4

🕐 Approx 25 minutes

This main dish salad features strips of warm rare beef, tossed in a lime-chilli dressing, and spooned on to raw spinach leaves. Cucumber salad surrounds the meat, and cherry tomatoes, spring onions, coriander and radishes garnish the whole thing. If you can't find bags of ready washed spinach in the supermarket, substitute any other easily prepared greens that you like.

Beef

Juice of 1 lime	*1 clove garlic, peeled and crushed*
1½ teaspoons Teriyaki Sauce	*Freshly ground pepper to taste*
1 slice ginger (¼-inch/0.5-cm thick), peeled and crushed	*1 goose skirt steak*

In a glass baking dish, combine all the ingredients except the meat. Turn the meat in this mixture and let it marinate until you're ready to cook it.

Dressing

Juice of 1 lime	crushed
¼ teaspoon Chinese chilli sauce	Pinch sugar
1 slice ginger and 1 clove garlic,	¼ teaspoon Teriyaki sauce

Combine in a screw-top jar and shake well. Refrigerate until needed.

Cucumber

1 long cucumber, peeled, halved, seeded and sliced	Dash Soy sauce
	Pinch sugar
1 chilli pepper, cored, seeded and sliced as thin as possible	1 tablespoon rice wine vinegar
	2 tablespoons water

Toss all ingredients together. Chill until needed.

Salad

Washed, dried spinach leaves	Sliced spring onions
Halved cherry tomatoes	Chopped fresh coriander
Sliced radishes	

To Cook and Assemble

1   Heat a ridged grill pan until hot. (Or, you could grill the meat on the outdoor barbecue.) With tongs, pull the meat out of the baking dish. Blot the meat on paper towels to dry it. Save the marinade juices. Sear the meat on both sides (about 1½ minutes on each side), using tongs to turn it.

2   With a small basting brush, brush the top of the steak with the marinade. Turn and cook (brushing the top side each time you turn the meat) for another 3–4 minutes on each side. It is *medium-rare* when it feels springy – not mushy – when poked in the centre with your finger. Transfer to a carving board and allow to rest for 3–4 minutes.

3   Carve in thin slices, slightly on the diagonal, against the grain. Cut the longest slices in half, crosswise. Put the slices in a bowl and pour over them any juices that have accumulated on the board. Pour the lime-chilli garlic sauce over the beef slices and toss with 2 spoons to combine.

4   Line an attractive platter with the spinach leaves. Arrange the beef slices on the leaves; pour and scrape all the juices over them. Surround with the cucumber salad, the halved cherry tomatoes and the radishes, and sprinkle with the sliced spring onion and chopped fresh coriander.

> To get the maximum juice from a lemon or lime, pierce it in a few places with a fork or thin skewer and then give it a few seconds in the microwave, or warm it briefly in a bowl of hot water. Then, with your palm, press and turn it a few times on your work surface. Halve the fruit, stick a fork into the cut half, and squeeze around the fork to release the juices.

TANDOORI PORK

⊕ Marinate as long (or as short) as you wish
½ hour (excluding marination)

Tandoori paste is available from supermarkets. Add it to some yoghurt, dredge a trimmed pork fillet thoroughly in the mixture and leave to marinate while you prepare the rest of the meal, set the table, etc. Of course, if you wish you can put the meat into the marinade in the morning, or even the night before. Long marinating produces a really zesty flavour, but even a short stint in the yoghurt-tandoori mixture results in a delicious piece of meat. The roasting takes less than half an hour. Left-overs are terrific in sandwiches or served cold with salad.

1 pork tenderloin (approx 1 lb/450 g)	3 tablespoons tandoori paste 8 oz/225 g low-fat yoghurt

1   Preheat oven to 475°F, 240°C, Gas Mark 9.
2   Trim the tenderloin carefully.
3   Mix the tandoori paste and yoghurt in a glass baking dish. Dredge the tenderloin with the mixture and leave to marinate until you are ready to roast it.
4   Line the grill tray with foil, shiny side up. Pour some water into the grill tray to a depth of ½ inch/1 cm. Put the rack on the tray. Place the meat on the rack.

5   Cook the tenderloin on the rack in the hot oven for approximately 20–25 minutes, basting and turning the meat occasionally during the roasting.
6   Allow to rest for approximately 5 minutes. Slice across the grain, slightly on the diagonal.

· ROASTED HONEY-MUSTARD TENDERLOIN

🕐 Approx ½ hour

Here is another quick-roasted pork tenderloin, this time without a preliminary marination. The mixture of honey and mustard is a perfect complement to the meat.

¾ tablespoon honey	1 tablespoon mustard
Juice of ¼ lemon	Freshly ground pepper to taste
1 clove garlic, minced	1 pork tenderloin, carefully
¼ teaspoon Soy sauce	trimmed
Pinch cayenne pepper	

---

1   Preheat the oven to 475°F, 240°C, Gas Mark 9.
2   Whisk together all the ingredients except the meat. Coat the tenderloin with the mustard-honey mixture.
3   Line the grill tray with the foil, shiny side up. Pour some water into the grill tray to a depth of ½ inch/1 cm. Put the rack on the tray. Place the meat on the rack.
4   Roast for 20–25 minutes, basting and turning halfway through.
5   Allow to rest for approximately 5 minutes, then slice slightly on the diagonal, across the grain, and serve.

BARBECUED PORK TENDERLOIN, CHINESE STYLE

🕐 Approx ½ hour

Hoi Sin sauce is Chinese Barbecue Sauce, and fat-free versions are available in jars from many supermarkets and speciality shops. Mixed with ketchup and orange juice concentrate, it gives the quick-roasted pork a lipsmacking sweet-and-sour flavour.

---

3 tablespoons Hoi Sin sauce	concentrate, thawed
3 tablespoons ketchup	1 pork tenderloin, approx
3 tablespoons frozen orange juice	1 lb/450 g, carefully trimmed

---

1   Preheat the oven to 475°F, 240°C, Gas Mark 9.
2   Combine all the ingredients except the pork in a glass baking dish. Dredge the tenderloin in the mixture and leave until you are ready to cook it.
3   Line the grill tray with foil, shiny side up. Pour some water into the grill tray to a depth of ½ inch/1 cm. Put the rack on the tray. Place the meat on the rack. Roast the tenderloin on the rack for 20–25 minutes, turning and basting occasionally.
4   Allow to rest for approximately 5 minutes. Slice across the grain, slightly on the diagonal, and serve.

PIPERADE PORK STEAKS

Makes 4 steaks

Tomato-Pepper Conserve: 20 minutes
Pork (excluding optional chilling time): 15 minutes

Boneless, loin pork steaks can be butterflied, stuffed with an interesting mixture, then breaded and grilled until crispy in no time at all. If you can, stuff them and dredge them in the breadcrumbs *before* you set the table and prepare the rest of the meal. The breading adheres a little better during the grilling if the steaks spend some time in the fridge. If time is short, don't worry, the recipe will still work nicely. *Piperade* refers to the tomato-pepper filling.

4 boneless loin pork steaks, ½–¾-inch/1–1.5 cm thick, trimmed of all fat	Grated Parmesan cheese
	2 egg whites
	Tomato-Pepper Conserve
Salt and pepper	(see page 102)
Plain breadcrumbs	Watercress

1   Preheat the grill to its highest setting. Line the grill tray with foil, shiny side up. Place the rack on the tray.
2   Butterfly the pork steaks: place them flat on your work surface. Put your palm firmly on a steak. With a very sharp knife, carefully slice the steak almost through so that it opens like a book. Sprinkle the inside with salt and pepper. Repeat with the remaining steaks.
3   Combine the breadcrumbs and Parmesan on a plate. Season with freshly ground pepper. Put the egg whites into a shallow bowl and beat lightly with a fork.
4   Open each steak and fill with a spoonful of the tomato-pepper conserve. Close up the steaks and press the edges together. Dredge the individual-filled steak in the crumbs,

coating each side and the edges well; then dip both sides and the edges into the egg white and dredge again with the crumb mixture. Have a plate on hand so that as each steak is ready, it can rest on the plate. (If you have time, refrigerate the steaks for ½–1 hour, but it is not necessary if time is short.)

5   Grill the steaks 5 inches/12.5 cm from the heating element for 2–3 minutes on each side, until browned and crusty. Serve at once, on a watercress garnished platter.

PORK STEAKS STUFFED WITH FRIED APPLES

Makes 4 steaks

Apples: 20 minutes
Pork (excluding optional chilling time): 15 minutes

Pork and apples combine well. Butterflied loin steaks stuffed with 'fried' apples and onions are exceptionally pleasing. You might want to serve them with additional fried apples and a nice heap of mashed potatoes.

4 boneless loin pork steaks, ½–¾-inch/1–1.5 cm thick, trimmed of all fat	Grated Parmesan cheese 2 egg whites Fried Apples (see page 111)
Salt and pepper Plain breadcrumbs	Watercress

1   Preheat the grill to its highest setting. Line the grill tray with foil, shiny side up. Place the rack on the tray.
2   Butterfly the pork steaks: place them flat on your work surface. Put your palm firmly on a steak. With a very sharp knife, carefully slice the steak almost through so that it opens like a book. Sprinkle the inside with salt and pepper. Repeat with the remaining steaks.
3   Combine the breadcrumbs and Parmesan on a plate. Season with freshly ground pepper. Put the egg whites into a shallow bowl and beat lightly with a fork.
4   Open each steak and fill with a spoonful of the Fried Apples. Close up the steak and press the edges together. Dredge each filled steak in the crumbs, coating each side and the edges well; then dip both sides and the edges into the egg white and dredge again with the crumb mixture. Have a plate on hand so that as each steak is ready, it can rest on the plate. (If you have time, refrigerate the steaks for ½–1 hour, but it is not necessary if time is short.)

5   Grill the steaks 5 inches/12.5 cm from the heating element for 2–3 minutes on each side, until browned and crusty. Serve at once, garnished with watercress.

PORK STEAKS STUFFED WITH MUSHROOMS

Makes 4 steaks

Mushrooms: 15 minutes
Pork (excluding optional chilling time): 20 minutes

Try smearing the inside of a butterflied pork steak with Dijon mustard, then adding a spoonful of sautéed mushrooms before sealing and breading the steaks and grilling them until crisp.

4 boneless loin pork steaks, ½–¾-inch/1–1.5 cm thick, trimmed of all fat	Plain breadcrumbs Grated Parmesan cheese 2 egg whites
Salt and pepper 2 teaspoons Dijon mustard	4 tablespoons Sautéed Mushrooms (see below)

1   Preheat the grill to its highest setting. Line the grill tray with foil, shiny side up. Place the rack on the tray.
2   Butterfly the pork steaks: place them flat on your work surface. Put your palm firmly on a steak. With a very sharp knife, carefully slice the steak almost through so that it opens like a book. Sprinkle the inside with salt and pepper, and spread ¼ teaspoon mustard on the inside of the steak. Repeat with the remaining steaks.
3   Combine the breadcrumbs and Parmesan on a plate. Season with freshly ground pepper. Put the egg whites into a shallow bowl together with 1 teaspoon Dijon mustard and beat lightly with a fork.
4   Open each steak and fill with a spoonful of the mushrooms. Close up the steaks and press the edges together. Dredge each filled steak in the crumbs, coating each side and the edges well; then dip both sides and the edges into the egg white and dredge again with the crumb mixture. Have a plate on hand so that as each steak is ready, it can rest on the plate. (If you have time, refrigerate the steaks for ½–1 hour, but it is not necessary if time is short.)
5   Grill the steaks 5 inches/12.5 cm from the heating element for 3 minutes on each side, until browned and crusty. Serve at once.

SAUTÉED MUSHROOMS

🕐 15 minutes

1–1½ lbs/450–700 g mushrooms (the more types of mushroom, the more interesting the flavour) 2–3 fl oz/50–75 ml stock	2–3 fl oz/50–75 ml dry sherry Splash or two Soy sauce (or Teriyaki sauce) Freshly ground pepper to taste

1 Leave button mushrooms whole if desired – larger mushrooms may be sliced or cut into quarters or eighths. If you use fresh shiitakes, trim off the tough stalks.
2 Spread out the mushrooms in a heavy bottomed pan, then pour in the liquids. Cook over a high heat, stirring. The mushrooms will release a great deal of liquid. Reduce the heat a little and keep on cooking, stirring occasionally, until the liquid has been absorbed and the mushrooms are 'frying' in their own juices. Never let the mushrooms scorch, burn or stick to the pan. Season with pepper. After stuffing the pork, save the left-over mushrooms to serve alongside the meat.

PORK STEAKS STUFFED WITH CHEESE

Makes 4 steaks

🕐 (excluding optional chill time) 20 minutes

Seal a small slice of mozzarella cheese in a butterflied pork loin steak, then bread it and grill it. When you cut into it with your knife, the melted cheese oozes out in a most gratifying way.

4 boneless loin pork steaks, ½–¾-inch/1–1.5-cm thick, trimmed of all fat Salt and pepper Plain breadcrumbs	Grated Parmesan cheese 2 egg whites 4 (¼-inch/0.5-cm thick each) slices mozzarella cheese, ¼–½ oz/5–10 g each

1 Preheat the grill to its highest setting. Line the grill tray with foil, shiny side up. Place the rack on the tray.
2 Butterfly the pork steaks: place them flat on your work surface. Put your palm firmly on a steak. With a very sharp knife, carefully slice the steak almost through so that it opens like a book. Sprinkle the inside with salt and pepper. Repeat with the remaining steaks.

3   Combine the breadcrumbs and Parmesan on a plate. Season
    with freshly ground pepper. Put the egg whites into a
    shallow bowl and beat lightly with a fork.

4   Trim the cheese slices so that they fit into the butterflied
    steaks. Open each steak and put a slice of mozzarella cheese
    into each one. Close up the steaks and press the edges
    together. Dredge each filled steak in the crumbs, coating each
    side and the edges well; then dip both sides and the edges
    into the egg white and dredge again with the crumb mixture.
    Have a plate on hand so that as each steak is ready, it can rest
    on the plate. (If you have time, refrigerate the steaks for ½–
    1 hour, but it is not necessary if time is short.)

5   Grill the steaks 5 inches/12.5 cm from the heating element for
    3 minutes on each side, until browned and crusty. Serve at
    once.

PORK-APPLE SAUSAGE PATTIES WITH FRIED APPLES

Makes 12 patties

Pan fried: 35 minutes
Grilled: 20 minutes

In my old Fat-Cuisine days, one of my favourite meals was pork
sausage served with fried apples and mashed potatoes. Talk
about rustic comfort! Here is that comfort, redesigned to be
beneficial to your health and waistline. The sausage patties are
made of lean minced pork mixed with apples, cider, mint, chillies
and lemon, and then pan sautéed in a mixture of cider and
calvados, which gives them a beautifully glazed finish. If you
want to save time and effort, grill them instead of pan sautéing –
they will still be marvellous.

---

*8 oz/225 g Granny Smith apples,
  peeled and roughly diced*
3 tablespoons medium-dry cider
¼ teaspoon crushed dried chillies
2 tablespoons chopped fresh parsley
2 tablespoons shredded fresh mint
Juice of ½ small lemon
2 cloves garlic
Salt and pepper to taste
6 tablespoons dry breadcrumbs
1 lb/450 g lean minced pork

*Additional breadcrumbs for
  dredging*
*Approx 1 pt/570 ml stock or mixed
  stock and water*
*Approx ½ pt/300 ml medium-dry
  cider*
*A few tablespoons Calvados –
  optional*
*Fried apples and onions
  (see page 111)*

---

1   Combine the apples, cider, chillies, parsley, mint, lemon juice and garlic in the container of a food processor. Blend until puréed.
2   Combine the apple mixture, salt, pepper, 6 tablespoons of breadcrumbs and pork and mix very well. Fry a tiny piece (use no fat!) and taste. Adjust seasonings if necessary.
3   Sprinkle several tablespoons of breadcrumbs on to a plate. Season lightly with salt and pepper. Form the pork mixture into approximately 12 plump, oval patties and dredge each thoroughly in the crumbs. Place on a large plate in one layer and refrigerate until you are ready to cook them.
4   Choose a large, heavy, non-reactive frying pan that will hold as many patties as you want to cook in one layer. Film it with stock to a depth of ¹⁄₁₆ inch/0.12 cm. Heat. When very hot, put in the patties. Cook on a moderately high heat until crusty on one side (about 3 minutes), then turn carefully (using a fish slice to loosen and turn them) and cook for a similar length of time on the second side until crusty brown. Replenish the stock augmented with splashes of cider and Calvados as needed. (The cider foams up when you add it to the hot pan, but that's no problem.) When browned, pour in a few ounces of stock, cider and Calvados, and cook on a medium heat, turning the patties carefully with the fish slice occasionally, for 3 minutes or so.
5   Cover and cook over a moderate heat for 10 minutes. (Uncover to turn the patties occasionally.) After 10 minutes, uncover and cook for 1–2 minutes more, until they are beautifully glazed, and the pan juices are scant, thick and syrupy. Remove to a platter and cover loosely with a tent of foil to keep warm.
6   Add the remaining stock, cider and Calvados to the frying pan and boil rapidly, scraping up all the browned bits, until you have a thick, syrupy, savoury sauce. Put the fried apples on to a serving platter and top with the pork patties. Pour the pan sauce over the patties and serve at once with mashed potatoes, if desired.

Note: For this recipe and the next, 1 lb/450 g of meat makes 12 patties. You might consider freezing half of them uncooked, for another time. They may be cooked directly from the frozen state: cook under a hot grill with the grill tray in the middle position for 7–10 minutes on each side. (To test if they are done, poke a thin metal skewer into the centre of one of the patties and leave for 2 seconds. Pull it out and hold the skewer against the centre of your lower lip. If cold, or barely warm, the patty is not done. If hot, it is done.)

Into the Pocket

Both the pork-apple patties (previous recipe) and the pork-courgette patties (recipe follows) are wonderful when stuffed into pitta pockets. Put a pork-apple patty into a pitta pocket and top with Fried Apples, or put a pork-courgette patty into a pitta pocket, and top with braised cabbage. What a satisfying sandwich this makes! As an American, I believe that the only proper sandwich is one that makes you open your mouth wide in order to encompass a good cross section, and then delivers a nice, juicy, interesting mouthful.

❄ PORK-COURGETTE SAUSAGE PATTIES WITH BRAISED CABBAGE

Makes 12 patties

Pan fried: 45 minutes
Grilled: 30 minutes

Another comforting, bistro-type, pork-sausage patty – this time cooked with red wine and served on a bed of braised cabbage. As with the previous recipe, the pork can be grilled rather than pan fried. (Cook the cabbage while they grill.) The courgettes stretch the meat and help to give the pork a juicy texture, but you will not particularly taste the courgettes in the finished dish. If you like, cook as many patties as you wish to eat, then freeze the rest uncooked for another day. See note, page 61 for directions on cooking the patties from the frozen state.

8 oz/225 g courgettes, sliced	1 lb/450 g lean minced pork
3 tablespoons red wine	Additional breadcrumbs for
¼ teaspoon crushed dried chillies	dredgings
2 tablespoons chopped fresh parsley	Approx 1 pt/570 ml stock or mixed
2 tablespoons chopped fresh basil	stock and water
Juice of ½ small lemon	Approx ½ pt/300 ml red vermouth
1 clove garlic, peeled	6–8 oz/175–225 g white cabbage,
Salt and pepper to taste	cored and shredded
6 tablespoons dry breadcrumbs	Pinch cayenne pepper – optional

1   Combine the courgettes, red wine, chillies, parsley, basil, lemon juice and garlic in the container of a food processor. Blend until puréed.
2   Combine the courgette mixture, salt, pepper, 6 tablespoons breadcrumbs and pork and mix very well. Fry a tiny piece (use no fat!) and taste. Adjust seasonings if necessary.
3   Sprinkle several tablespoons of breadcrumbs on to a plate. Season lightly with salt and pepper. Form the pork mixture into approximately 12 plump, oval patties and dredge each thoroughly in the crumbs. Place on a large plate in one layer and refrigerate until you are ready to cook them.
4   Choose a large, heavy, non-reactive frying pan that will hold as many patties as you want to cook in one layer. Film it with stock to a depth of $\frac{1}{16}$ inch/0.12 cm. Heat. When very hot, put in the patties. Cook on a moderately high heat until crusty on one side (about 3 minutes). Then turn carefully (using a fish slice to loosen and turn them) and cook for a similar length of time on the second side until crusty brown. Replenish the stock augmented with splashes of red vermouth as needed. The red vermouth, when added, will fume and sputter: the alcohol quickly boils away and leaves a syrupy essence that helps brown the patties and gives them a delicious coating. When browned, pour in a few ounces of stock and red vermouth and cook on a medium heat, turning the patties carefully with the fish slice occasionally, for approximately 3 minutes. Carefully remove the patties to a plate.
5   Stir the cabbage into the pan juices. Add some more stock and vermouth if the pan is almost dry. Season the cabbage with a bit of salt and pepper and a pinch of cayenne pepper if you like it hot. Return the pork patties to the bed of cabbage in the pan. Cover and cook over a moderate heat for 7–10 minutes. Turn the patties occasionally. After 10 minutes, uncover for 1–2 minutes more, until the cabbage is tender, and the pan juices are scant, thick and syrupy. Serve at once, right out of the pan.

Chicken

If you want to practise healthy, fast chicken cookery, buy quick-cooking chicken parts and remove *all* the skin and fat before introducing the meat to the pan. Chicken breasts can be purchased already skinned and boned, but they usually need more trimming at home to remove all vestiges of skin, fat and gristle.

It's important to remember that the skin of the chicken has an underlayer of fat and has no place in a slimming or maintenance regime. Free-range, bone-in chicken thighs are my current favourite chicken piece: these you must skin meticulously yourself, but if you have a friendly and accommodating butcher, he may agree to do it for you. But you will still have to do some additional trimming at home to remove all traces of skin and fat. Skinless chicken thighs can be oven barbecued: simply arrange them in a baking dish in one layer, blanket them with an interesting combination of store-cupboard ingredients (see suggestions in the following recipes) and bake uncovered at 350°F, 180°C, Gas Mark 4 for 40–45 minutes. They need no attention, other than one or two quick bastings and they fill the kitchen with the most compelling aroma imaginable. This method is a great convenience: when you get home from work, you can immediately put the ingredients together, then throw the panful of chicken into the oven and let it cook, while you check the answer machine, read your mail, greet the cat, catch up on the kids and try to convince someone to set the table. If you are really organized, put the chicken in the baking dish and blanket it with its sauce in the morning, before you go to work. Then, when you get home, all you have to do is fling it into the oven. The chicken, of course, benefits flavourfully from its day of marination.

I've also developed a nifty way to pan-braise skinned chicken thighs. The classic way to pan-cook chicken pieces is to leave the skin *on* and to brown the parts in butter or oil, before adding the remaining ingredients and leaving to simmer. Then, all too often, the sauce is given a final enrichment with cream. Fat, upon fat, upon fat! My method revises the classic: first, simmer the skinned thighs in liquid in the pan, turning occasionally. As they simmer, the liquid reduces and the chicken gently cooks through. Finally the liquid cooks down to a rich essence, and the chicken becomes meltingly tender and beautifully browned and glazed. This method is easy, quick, extremely low in fat and absolutely delicious.

Hygiene Note: It is a good idea to keep a separate cutting board solely for poultry trimming and preparation. After each use, scrub with disinfectant, rinse very well with hot water, dry and store until the next time you prepare poultry. Never use the board for preparing vegetables or any other foods after it has been used for raw poultry.

Make Sunday special with a memorable breakfast: clockwise from upper right: smoked cod in mustard 'cream' sauce; mushrooms on toast; wheaten bread with honey.

Splendour in the grass: clockwise from upper right: pumpernickel bread; ham and cheese bread; chicken-potato salad; tuna-lemon-chutney pâté; couscous salad with smoked mackerel and oranges; chilled tomato-orange soup; Eton mess.

OVEN-BARBECUED CHICKEN

Makes 6 pieces

⏱ 50 minutes

Tomato passata from a box, chutney from a jar and a splash of lime: barbecue sauces don't get much easier than this. If you can't find lime, use half a small lemon instead.

4 fl oz/110 ml tomato passata	*Several dashes Tabasco sauce –*
1 jar curried fruit chutney	*optional*
(8½ oz/235g)	*6 skinned chicken thighs*
Juice and grated rind of ½ lime	

1   Preheat the oven to 350°F, 180°C, Gas Mark 4.
2   Combine thoroughly the tomato passata, curried fruit chutney, lime juice and lime rind and the Tabasco sauce if using.
3   Place the chicken, skinned side up, in a baking dish so that the chicken pieces do not touch each other. Season with freshly ground pepper.
4   Pour tomato-chutney mixture evenly over and around the chicken.
5   Bake uncovered for 40–45 minutes, basting once or twice during the baking.
6   Serve with crusty bread to soak up the delicious juices.

CHINESE OVEN-BARBECUED CHICKEN

Makes 6 pieces

⏱ 50 minutes

Soy sauce, honey, sherry and ginger give oven-barbecued chicken a stunning Chinese glaze.

2 fl oz/50 ml Soy sauce	*½ teaspoon dry mustard*
2 fl oz/50 ml runny mild honey	*1 teaspoon minced fresh ginger*
2 tablespoons lemon juice	*6 skinned chicken thighs*
2 tablespoons dry sherry	

1   Thoroughly combine all the ingredients except the chicken.
2   Toss the chicken and Soy sauce-honey mixture together, and let marinate while you preheat the oven to 350°F, 180°C, Gas Mark 4.
3   When the oven is preheated, arrange the chicken pieces skinned side up in a baking dish, so that they do not touch

each other. Pour and scrape any remaining marinade over and around the chicken.

4 Bake, uncovered, for 40–45 minutes, basting once or twice during the baking.

5 Serve the chicken with rice and gingered mushrooms (see page 106).

PAN-BRAISED CHICKEN WITH RED VERMOUTH

Makes 4 pieces

🕐 25 minutes

Red vermouth has both bitter-sweetness and herbal undertones; I think it makes an inspired cooking medium for pan-braised chicken thighs. The garlic, because it is simmered in the liquid along with the chicken, takes on a melting mellowness – there is none of the vulgar, acrid quality that comes with frying garlic in fat or oil.

4 chicken thighs, skinned and trimmed of all fat	2–3 cloves garlic, peeled and coarsely chopped
4 fl oz/110 ml stock	Salt and freshly ground pepper to taste
4 fl oz/110 ml red vermouth	

1 Arrange the chicken, skinned side down, in a heavy bottomed, non-reactive frying pan. Pour in the liquids and scatter the garlic pieces around the chicken. (The chicken should be in one uncrowded layer.) Bring to the boil.

2 Simmer uncovered, turning the chicken occasionally, for about 20 minutes. As it cooks, the liquid will reduce down considerably. When the juices are thick and syrupy, the chicken will brown nicely (turn it frequently at this point). When the chicken is meltingly tender, there is no pink at the bone and the garlic is very soft in a thick syrupy sauce, the dish is done. If, during the cooking, the liquid boils away, add a bit more as needed. If, on the other hand, the chicken is tender and cooked through, and there is a considerable amount of liquid left, remove the chicken to a plate, and boil the pan juices down. Then return the chicken to the sauce.

PAN-BRAISED CHICKEN WITH LEMON

Makes 4 pieces

🕐 25 minutes

In this variation the chicken is braised with lemon, stock and garlic. The garlic becomes gently mellow, the lemon and stock cook down to a creaminess and the flavour penetrates right to the bone of the chicken.

---

4 chicken thighs, skinned and trimmed of all fat	*2–3 cloves garlic, coarsely chopped*
4 fl oz/110 ml stock	*Salt and freshly ground pepper to taste*
Strained juice of 1 large lemon	

---

1 Arrange the chicken, skinned side down, in a heavy bottomed, non-reactive frying pan. Pour in the stock and half the lemon juice and scatter the garlic pieces around the chicken. (The chicken should be in one uncrowded layer.) Bring to the boil.
2 Simmer uncovered, turning the chicken occasionally, for about 20 minutes. As it cooks, the liquid will reduce down considerably. When the juices are thick and syrupy, the chicken will brown nicely (turn it frequently at this ponit). Squeeze in the remaining lemon juice and cook, turning the chicken constantly, for another minute or two. If, during the cooking, the liquid boils away, add a bit more as needed. If, on the other hand, the chicken is tender and cooked through, and there is a considerable amount of liquid left, remove the chicken to a plate and boil the pan juices down. Then return the chicken to the sauce.

PAN-BRAISED CHICKEN WITH APPLES

Makes 4 pieces

🕐 30 minutes

I tried to capture a hint of Normandy without any hints of fat – I'm not displeased with the result. Chicken, apples, cider and Calvados: who could ask for anything more?

4 chicken thighs, skinned and trimmed of all fat	2 shallots, minced
4 fl oz/110 ml stock	Salt and freshly ground pepper to taste
4 fl oz/110 ml medium dry cider	1 Granny Smith apple, peeled, cored and sliced into ¼-inch/ 0.5-cm thick wedges
2 fl oz/50 ml Calvados	
2 tablespoons orange liqueur, such as Cointreau or Grand Marnier	

1 Arrange the chicken, skinned side down, in a heavy bottomed, non-reactive frying pan. Pour in the liquids and scatter the shallots around the chicken. (The chicken should be in one uncrowded layer.) Season and then bring to the boil.

2 Simmer uncovered, turning the chicken occasionally, for about 15 minutes. As it cooks, the liquid will reduce down considerably. When the juices are thick and syrupy, the chicken will brown nicely. Add the apple and cook (turning the chicken frequently) until the chicken is tender and cooked through, and the apple is soft. If, during the cooking, the liquid boils away, add a bit more as needed. If, on the other hand, the chicken is tender and cooked through, and there is a considerable amount of liquid left, remove the chicken to a plate, and boil the pan juices down. Then return the chicken to the sauce.

PAN-BRAISED GINGER CHICKEN

Makes 4 pieces

🕐 25 minutes

Five spice powder – that fragrant Chinese blend of clove, anise, fennel, ginger and cinnamon – is available in supermarkets (look on the spice shelf). I've added fresh ginger as well, and a dash of cayenne pepper.

4 skinned chicken thighs	crushed
4 tablespoons dry sherry	2 cloves garlic, minced
2 tablespoons Soy sauce	Pinch or two cayenne pepper
4 fl oz/110 ml stock	¼ teaspoon five spice powder
1 slice fresh ginger, peeled and	

1 Arrange the chicken, skinned side down, in a heavy bottomed, non-reactive frying pan. Pour in the liquids, and scatter the remaining ingredients around the chicken. (The chicken should be in one uncrowded layer.) Bring gently to the boil.

2   Simmer uncovered, turning the chicken occasionally, for about 20 minutes according to size. As it cooks, the liquid will reduce down considerably. When the juices are thick and syrupy, the chicken will brown nicely (turn it frequently at this point). When the chicken is meltingly tender, there is no pink at the bone, and the garlic is very soft in a thick syrupy sauce, the dish is done. If, during the cooking, the liquid boils away, add a bit more as needed. If, on the other hand, the chicken is tender and cooked through, and there is a considerable amount of liquid left, remove the chicken to a plate, and boil the pan juices down. Then return the chicken to the sauce.

♡ QUICK-POACHED CHICKEN BREASTS
⏱ 15 minutes

Skinless, boneless chicken breasts can be poached in no time at all and then served with almost any of the quick Slim Cuisine sauces (see the index and the sauce chapter). Poached chicken is also excellent for chicken salads and sandwiches.

1 lb/450 g boneless, skinless chicken breasts	1 tablespoon Balsamic vinegar
½ pt/300 ml water or stock	1½ teaspoons Soy sauce
	Pinch cayenne pepper

1   Spread the chicken breasts out in one layer in a large, heavy bottomed frying pan or shallow flame-proof casserole. Combine the remaining ingredients and pour over the chicken. Cover the pan tightly and bring to the boil.
2   Immediately remove from the heat and allow to stand, covered, for 10 minutes.

Hygiene Note: Poached chicken salads and sandwiches are scrumptious, but not in packed lunches, destined to be carried around all day. Keep poached chicken chilled in the fridge until it's time to eat it, to avoid food poisoning.

Chicken Sandwiches to Cherish

Try sliced poached chicken breasts in pitta bread or a split baguette with one of the following:

Cannellini-Pimiento Sauce (see page 139)
Tomato-Pepper Conserve (see page 102)
Curried Apricot Spread and Watercress (see page 45)
Cucumber-Cherry Tomato Salsa (see page 131)
Sweet-and-Sour Peppers (see page 125)
Cole Slaw (see page 129)
Cucumber Salad (see page 128)
Creamy Herb Spread (see page 45)

CHICKEN-POTATO SALAD

25 minutes

Poached chicken breasts, steamed new potatoes, cucumbers and some vivid Oriental seasonings combine to make a lovely chicken-potato salad mixture to serve on a bed of spinach leaves, or other dark, leafy greens. This is best when the chicken and potatoes are still warm but the greens are crisp and cold.

Dressing

1½ teaspoons sugar	1 slice ginger, peeled and crushed
Juice of 2 limes	1–2 cloves garlic, peeled and
Juice of ½ orange	crushed
1 tablespoon Soy sauce	1 chilli pepper, minced – optional

Salad

4 oz/110 g new potatoes	1 cucumber, peeled, halved, seeded
2 quick-poached chicken breasts (see page 69)	and sliced thin

Garnish

Washed, dried young spinach leaves (or whatever salad greens you like) *Halved cherry tomatoes*	*Chopped fresh coriander, mint and parsley* *Sliced spring onions*

1   Combine dressing ingredients in a screw-top jar and shake well.
2   Steam potatoes until tender. Cut in half and – while they are still warm – toss with half of the dressing. Set aside.
3   Slice the chicken breasts on the diagonal, across the grain. Combine the sliced chicken with the cucumber. Toss with the remaining dressing. Combine the potatoes and the chicken-cucumber mixture.
4   To serve, line a platter with spinach. Spoon the chicken-potatoes over the greens. Surround with cherry tomatoes. Sprinkle generously with the herbs and sliced spring onions.

Fish

Fish is good food. High in the best protein, low in fat (even the fattiest fish is lower in fat than fatty meat or poultry – and fish fat is believed to be beneficial to the heart), quick and easy to cook, compatible with a myriad ingredients, it would seem to be an ideal food. In many parts of England the problem with fish is availability. In most areas, fresh fish choices are extremely limited, sometimes even totally non-existent. And sometimes the 'fresh' fish on offer is actually defrosted fish ('previously frozen' is the term usually employed). If it *is* fresh in the sense of never having been frozen, the time that has elapsed between the poor fish's stay in its natural watery habitat and its appearance on the supermarket fish counter may be long enough to make the word *fresh* totally inappropriate. I used to believe that fresh fish was the only kind to eat, and that frozen fish was an abomination. I'll admit my folly right now: I was wrong. Several years of childhood spent on the coast of New York's Long Island, several summers spent on the coast of Maine, and travel to famously fishy paradises like Hong Kong, Japan and the Côte d'Azur underline my passion for the truly fresh, but 'previously frozen'? When were they thawed, how long have they been languishing dejectedly on the fish counter, and why does the odour hovering around the fish department remind me of Unhygenix, the fish-monger in the Asterix books? In such cases, give me frozen, please. I can carry it home solidly frozen and store it safely in my freezer until I'm ready to cook it. The best way to deal with frozen fish is to take an insulated bag containing a few frozen cold blocks with you to the supermarket. Carry the fish home in the bag along with any other frozen foods you have purchased and immediately pack it all away in the coldest part of your freezer. There it will wait, until the urge for a fish dinner strikes. Cook the fish right from the frozen state. I think you will be delighted with how fresh frozen fish can taste – especially compared with the poor old flabby fillets that decay – even as we watch them – on many fish counters. And you will certainly be delighted with the speed with which these dishes can be prepared.

 ## FISH SAUCE FOR PASTA

Yields 3 pt/1.7 l

🕐 30 minutes

A beautiful saucy stew, this recipe will sauce approx 1 lb/450 g of pasta. To save time, put half the pasta water in a pot, the other half in the kettle, then combine when boiling. Start the sauce in a heavy bottomed pan; both pasta and sauce should be ready at the same time. If you wish, make up a batch of the sauce *without* the fish and store it, in small portions, in the freezer. Then, at dinner time, put on the pasta, defrost as much sauce as you want in the microwave, transfer to the hob, add some fish when the sauce is simmering and finish the recipe.

---

1 large onion, chopped
3–4 sun-dried tomatoes diced (use scissors) – optional
3 cloves garlic, crushed
15 fl oz/400 ml stock
4 fl oz/110 ml white vermouth
1 small can (6½ oz/185 g) red peppers (pimientos), drained and chopped
1 large can (1 lb 12 oz/800 g) Italian tomatoes, well drained, and cut into strips
1 can (12 oz/350 g) chopped Italian tomatoes

2-inch/5-cm strip orange peel
1 bay leaf
Salt and freshly ground pepper to taste
1 tablespoon tomato purée
3–4 tablespoons shredded fresh basil
3–4 tablespoons chopped fresh parsley
1 lb/450 g frozen white fish fillets (a mixture of cod and haddock works well)
4 oz/110 g frozen tiny cooked prawns – optional

---

1   Combine the onion, sun-dried tomatoes if using, garlic, and
    ½ pt/300 ml stock in a heavy bottomed pan. Cover and bring
    to the boil. Boil for 5–7 minutes. Uncover and simmer briskly
    until the onion is tender and the liquid is about gone. Pour in
    the vermouth and cook briskly, scraping up any browned
    bits, until it has almost evaporated.
2   Stir in the pimientos, tomatoes, orange peel, bay leaf, salt
    and pepper. Simmer uncovered for 10 minutes. Stir in the
    tomato purée, herbs and remaining stock. Place the fish
    fillets on top of the sauce. Season the fish with salt and
    pepper. Cover and simmer for 10 minutes, or until the fish is
    done. Remove the bay leaf and orange peel. If you are using
    the prawns, add them for the last 5 minutes. With a spoon
    break up the fish and stir it into the sauce. Serve over
    rigatoni, rigati or penne.

♡   **PROVENÇAL FISH AND**
          POTATO CASSEROLE

Serves 2–4

⏱ 30 minutes

You will be astonished at how good this tastes, even though it is
made with *frozen fish fillets*. For someone like me, brought up on
the sanctity of sparkling fresh, just-caught fish, this dish is a
revelation, and a graphic reminder to keep an open mind in
culinary matters. Good fish stock is available in the chill cabinet of
many supermarkets, otherwise use vegetable stock, or even
chicken stock. Properly ripe tomatoes make the casserole very
special indeed, but never, never resort to those unripened,
tennis-ball-like imposters that are – all too often – the only so-
called tomatoes on offer. (On tomato matters, I'll never compromise!) See page 20 for advice on having *good* tomatoes on hand at all
times, otherwise, substitute canned Italian tomatoes. The garlic
sauce can be prepared in advance, or – to save preparation time –
while the fish casserole is cooking.

1 large onion, cut in half and sliced
    into thin half-moons
2 cloves garlic, crushed
2–3 sun-dried tomatoes, diced –
    optional
Pinch crushed dried chillies
½ pint/300 ml stock
4 small potatoes (about 2 oz/50 g
    each), peeled and sliced
    ¼-inch/0.5-cm thick
Salt and pepper to taste

2 large ripe tomatoes, peeled, seeded
    and chopped
1–2 tablespoons shredded fresh basil
1 bay leaf
3-inch/7.5-cm strip orange zest
1 lb/450 g frozen white fish fillets
Approx 1 pt/570 ml boiling stock
Chopped parsley for garnish
Toasted slices of bread
Garlic sauce (see below)

1   Combine the onion, garlic, sun-dried tomatoes if using, chillies and ½ pt/300 ml stock in a Le Creuset 11½ inch/ 29 cm diameter Buffet Casserole, a Corning Ware 10 inch/ 25.5 cm deep flame-proof casserole or similar pot. Cover and bring to the boil. Boil for 5 minutes. Uncover and cook, briskly, until the onion is tender and brown, and the liquid almost gone.

2   Spread the onions evenly over the bottom of the casserole. Arrange the sliced potatoes over the onions. Season with salt and pepper. Spread the tomatoes over the potatoes. Add the basil, bay leaf and orange peel. Top with the frozen fish fillets and sprinkle on a bit more salt and pepper. Pour in enough boiling stock to just cover the vegetables. Cover the casserole.

3   Simmer for 20 minutes, or until the potatoes are tender, and the fish cooked through. Sprinkle with some chopped parsley. To serve, break up the fish with your serving spoon and ladle some broth, vegetables and fish into soup plates. Pass round the toast and the garlic sauce. Diners should spread a slice of toast with the sauce, and then drop the slice into their soup plate. The toast disintegrates and the sauce melds with the juices, adding texture and flavour.

♡ GARLIC SAUCE

Yields ⅓ pt/180 ml sauce

⊕ 15 minutes

This is a no-fat version of the garlicky, piquant, mayonnaise-like sauce served with fish soups and stews in the South of France. It's hard to say exactly what appears in the traditional version of this sauce – olive oil, certainly, along with chilli pepper and garlic. Many versions contain egg yolks, some contain breadcrumbs, others crushed cooked potato. Many versions include puréed fish liver. In other words, it is one of those recipes that has almost as many 'real' versions as there are cooks preparing it. My interpretation contains an infusion of garlic and chilli (cooked so that the garlic takes on a sweet, gentle character), along with bread for texture and tomato purée for its colour as well as for its taste and texture. The result is excellent, although the sauce contains no oil at all.

6–8 cloves garlic	trimmed of crust
Pinch or two crushed dried chilli flakes	1 tablespoon tomato purée
½ pt/300 ml stock	2–4 fl oz/50–110 ml boiling vegetable stock
2 thin slices bakery white bread,	

1   Combine the garlic, chillies and 4 fl oz/110 ml stock in a frying pan. Cover and bring to the boil. Boil for 7–10 minutes. Uncover and simmer until the garlic cloves are meltingly tender and the stock is greatly reduced and syrupy.
2   Scrape the garlic and all the pan juices into the bowl of a food processor. Tear the bread into pieces and add it along with the tomato purée and 1–2 spoonfuls of the hot stock. Blend to a paste. Slowly blend in the remaining liquid until the mixture is the texture of a loose mayonnaise.

 ## SANDIE MITCHEL-KING'S FLAKED SMOKED COD IN MUSTARD 'CREAM' SAUCE

Yields 1½ pts/900 ml

⏰ 15 minutes

My assistant, Sandie Mitchel-King, developed this recipe for creamy smoked cod, using the basic Slim Cuisine White Sauce, enriched with Dijon mustard. Her family enjoys gratins of flaked fish in a creamy sauce with a crunchy topping. The recipe can also be prepared with unsmoked cod fillets (or half-smoked fish, half-plain) and plain (no mustard) white sauce (see page 135) and a mashed potato topping instead of breadcrumbs.

4 pieces frozen smoked cod (approx 1½ lb/700 g)
1 carton (approx 18 fl oz/500 ml) skimmed milk
6 tablespoons skimmed milk powder

3 tablespoons cornflour
2 rounded tablespoons Dijon mustard
2 oz/50 g plain breadcrumbs

1 Preheat the grill.
2 Place the frozen fish in one layer in a microwave-proof dish together with 4 fl oz/110 ml milk. Cover with cling film. Microwave on high for approximately 6 minutes (checking halfway through) until the fish is just done.
3 In the mean time, measure the milk powder and cornflour into a 3½ pt/2 l, 7 inch/18 cm diameter top, opaque white-plastic measuring jug (see box, page 189).
4 With a wire whisk, whisk the remaining milk into the dry ingredients. Add the mustard. Beat well – you don't want lumps. And vigorous whisking helps prevent volcanic eruptions.
5 When the fish is cooked, strain the poaching liquid into the jug. Whisk. Cover the jug tightly with cling film and put it into the microwave. Cook on high for 3 minutes. Carefully uncover (avert your face and begin with the side away from you, to release the steam. Be careful – the steam is hot) and beat thoroughly. Re-cover tightly and microwave for another 2 minutes. Uncover again, whisk, re-cover and microwave for a final 1½–2 minutes, until boiled, thickened and smooth. Whisk and allow to stand for 3–4 minutes.
6 Meanwhile, flake the fish (remove the skin if necessary). Mix the fish into the sauce. Spread out the fish and sauce in a 10-inch/25.5-cm square, 2-inches/5-cm deep oven-proof dish. Evenly sprinkle on the breadcrumbs. Place under the hot grill for a few minutes until golden brown.

Steaming Fish in a Wok

A big wok with a lid (see page 24) is perfect for steaming fish fillets. Some woks come with a steaming rack; if not improvise by placing a small over-turned heat-proof bowl or plate on the bottom of the wok. Pour in some boiling water. Set your fish fillets on a larger heat-proof plate (it should fit nicely in the wok). Put the fish plate on the rack. Obviously, the boiling water should reach a level just below the fish plate. Cover the wok tightly and steam. Frozen cod fillets will be ready in approximately 20 minutes, plaice or lemon sole in approximately 10 minutes. Replenish the water if it starts to boil away.

To test if the fillet is done, insert a thin bladed knife into the centre. It should be opaque all the way through. Over-cooking ruins the delicacy and good taste of the fish so watch it carefully. After you have cooked frozen fish a few times by this simple method, you will develop a feeling for it.

If you want to prepare any of these steamed fish recipes with *fresh* fish (it must be impeccably fresh), measure the fillet at its thickest point, and give it 5 minutes cooking time for each ½ inch/1 cm of thickness. Most of the steamed fish recipes that follow are for one fillet, but you can steam up to 4 at a time in a wok. Simply multiply the ingredients by 2, 3 or 4 if desired.

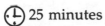 ## STEAMED FISH FILLETS WITH TOMATOES AND HERBS

Serves 1

⏲ 25 minutes

Steamed fillets of cod, with simple, fresh ingredients, make a very pleasing quick meal. If you have no perfectly ripe tomatoes or fresh herbs, save this recipe for another time.

1 piece frozen cod fillet	*and diced*
1 tablespoon fresh lemon juice	*Sprinkling of fresh herbs: chives,*
Salt and freshly ground pepper to	*parsley, tarragon, chervil –*
taste	*whatever is available*
1 medum tomato, skinned, seeded	

1   Remove the fish from the freezer and place it on a flat, heat-proof plate that will fit into your wok (see box, page 77). Sprinkle the fish with lemon juice and salt and pepper. Allow to sit for 5 minutes.
2   In the mean time, fill the bottom of the wok with water. Put the steamer rack or an over-turned small plate in the wok. Bring the water to the boil.
3   Top the fish with the tomato and herbs.
4   Put the fish plate on the rack. Cover tightly and steam for approximately 20 minutes, or until the fish is just done. Serve at once.

♡ STEAMED FISH FILLETS WITH ORANGES

Serves 1

🕐 25 minutes

I love the delicacy of cod and I think oranges and just a hint of nutmeg complement it very well.

1 piece frozen cod fillet	taste
Juice of ½ orange	½ seedless orange, peeled of all rind
Slivered zest of ¼ orange	and pith, and separated in
Pinch freshly grated nutmeg	segments
Salt and freshly ground pepper to	

1   Remove the fish from the freezer and place it on a flat, heat-proof plate that will fit into your wok (see box, page 77). Sprinkle the fish with the orange juice, orange zest, nutmeg, salt and pepper. Allow to sit for 5 minutes.
2   In the mean time, fill the bottom of the wok with water. Put the steamer rack or an over-turned small plate in the wok. Bring the water to the boil.
3   Top the fish with the orange segments.
4   Put the fish plate on the rack. Cover tightly and steam for approximately 20 minutes, or until the fish is just done. Serve at once.

♡ STEAMED FISH FILLETS WITH COURGETTES AND MUSHROOMS

Serves 1

⏱ 25 minutes

Vary the vegetables according to availability: sliced fennel (sprinkle on the feathery leaves as well); small broccoli florets; peeled, seeded cucumber slices (use snipped fresh dill with the cucumbers). Stand in the greengrocer department and let your imagination roam free.

---

1 piece frozen cod fillet	1 button mushroom, sliced thin
1 tablespoon each of lemon juice and orange juice	1 small tomato, skinned, seeded and diced
Salt and freshly ground pepper	Chopped parsley
½ small courgette, sliced thin	1 spring onion, trimmed and sliced

---

1   Remove the fish from the freezer and place it on a flat, heat-proof plate that will fit into your wok (see box, page 77). Sprinkle the fish with the lemon and orange juice, salt and pepper. Allow to sit for 5 minutes.
2   In the mean time, fill the bottom of the wok with water. Put the steamer rack or an over-turned small plate in the wok. Bring the water to the boil.
3   Top the fish with the courgette, mushroom, tomato, parsley and spring onion.
4   Put the fish plate on the rack. Cover well and steam for approximately 20 minutes, or until the fish is done. Serve at once.

♡ STEAMED FISH FILLETS, CHINESE STYLE

Serves 1

⏱ 30 minutes

After the fish has steamed with its Chinese seasonings, tip the juices into a small saucepan and boil until reduced and thickened, then pour the resulting beautiful sauce over the fillet.

---

1 piece frozen cod fillet	1 thin slice ginger, peeled and crushed
1 teaspoon Hoi Sin sauce	
1 teaspoon Soy sauce	1 small clove garlic, crushed
2 tablespoons stock	1 spring onion, trimmed and sliced

---

1   Put the fish on a heat-proof plate that fits into your wok. Combine all the remaining ingredients and pour them over the fish. Allow to stand for 5 minutes.
2   In the mean time, fill the bottom of the wok with water. Put the steamer rack or an over-turned small plate in the wok. Bring the water to the boil.
3   Put the fish plate on the rack. Cover well and steam for approximately 20 minutes, or until the fish is just done.
4   With a fish slice, transfer the fish to a warm plate. Cover loosely. Tip all the juices from the steaming plate into a small saucepan or frying pan. Boil rapidly until reduced by half. Pour over the fish and serve at once.

♡   # FIVE SPICE STEAMED COD

Serves 1

🕐 25 minutes

When I open a jar of five spice powder and the sweet, complex fragrance wafts up and hits me in the nose, I'm immediately transported back to my childhood. It's like magic dust, that powder: New York's Chinatown is there, in the little jar, and I can picture myself as a child trudging through the endlessly fascinating streets. I never get tired of it – the only thing I find more evocative is melting chicken fat with onions and *that* I never touch any more. Do be careful, though. A pinch of five spice is exquisite – too much is overpowering.

1 piece of frozen cod fillet	1 clove garlic, crushed
½ teaspoon Soy sauce	1 thin slice ginger, peeled and
1 teaspoon dry sherry	minced fine
Pinch five spice powder	1 spring onion, trimmed and sliced
Pinch cayenne pepper	

1   Choose a plate that will hold the fillet, and will fit into your wok (see box, page 77). Place the frozen cod fillet on the plate. Sprinkle the Soy sauce and sherry over it, along with the five spice powder, cayenne pepper, garlic, ginger and spring onion. Allow to sit for 5 minutes.
2   In the mean time, fill the bottom of your wok with water. Put the steamer rack or an over-turned small plate in the water. Bring to the boil. Put the fish plate on to the rack or over-turned bowl. Cover and steam for 20 minutes, or until the fish is just done.

STEAMED SOLE WITH CREAMY TARRAGON SAUCE

Makes 2 fillets and 1 pt/570 ml sauce

25 minutes

Steamed fish fillets can be lifted off their steaming plate and set on a sauce (it's nice if the sauce is *under* rather than *over* the fish.) Here, steamed lemon sole (you could substitute plaice if you wish) is set on a creamy tarragon sauce. (See page 135 for a thorough discussion of basic Slim Cuisine White Sauce.)

2 fillets of frozen lemon sole	Salt and freshly ground pepper to
½ teaspoon dried tarragon,	taste
crumbled	Pinch allspice
Juice of 1 lemon	Creamy Tarragon Sauce (see below)

1   Choose a plate that will hold the fillets in one layer and that will fit in your steamer arrangement. (See box, page 77) Place the frozen sole on the plate. Crumble the tarragon into the lemon juice and pour over the fish.
2   Sprinkle the remaining seasonings evenly over the frozen fish. Leave to marinate while you make the sauce (see below).
3   Fill the bottom of the wok with water and bring to the boil. (When boiling the water should not touch the bottom of the plate.) Put the steamer rack or a small over-turned plate on the bottom of the wok. Put the fish plate on to the steamer rack or over-turned plate. Cover and steam for approximately 10 minutes or until the fish is *just* done.
4   Tilt the plate and pour any collected juices into a jug. Whisk the juices into the tarragon sauce. Pour some of the sauce on to the centre of a plate. With a fish slice lift a fillet and centre it on the sauce. Repeat with the second piece of fish. Serve at once.

♡ ⊠ CREAMY TARRAGON SAUCE

Yields 1 pt/570 ml

🕐 10 minutes

---

4 *spring onions, trimmed and sliced*	3 *tablespoons skimmed milk powder*
4 *fl oz/110 g dry white vermouth*	1½ *tablespoons cornflour*
½ *pt/300 ml stock*	*Salt and freshly ground pepper to*
½ *teaspoon dried tarragon*	*taste*
Pinch ground allspice	9 *fl oz/275 ml skimmed milk*

---

1   Combine the spring onions, vermouth, stock, tarragon and allspice in a frying pan. Cover and boil for 5 minutes. Uncover and simmer briskly until the onions are tender and the liquid is greatly reduced and syrupy. Set aside.
2   Measure the milk powder and cornflour into a 3½ pt/2 l, 7-inch/18-cm diameter top, opaque white-plastic measuring jug (see box, page 189). Sprinkle on the salt and pepper.
3   With a wire whisk, mix the milk thoroughly into the dry ingredients – you don't want lumps and you don't want volcanic eruptions. Cover the jug tightly with cling film.
4   Microwave on high for 3 minutes. Carefully uncover (avert your face and begin with the side away from you, to release the steam. Be careful – the steam is hot) and whisk well. Re-cover tightly and microwave for another 2 minutes. Uncover carefully, whisk, re-cover and microwave for a final 1½–2 minutes until boiled, thickened and smooth. Uncover and mix in the tarragon mixture.
5   Allow to stand for 3–4 minutes, whisking occasionally.

♡ STEAMED COD, MEXICAN STYLE WITH PIQUANT TOMATO SAUCE

Makes 2 pieces

🕐 35 minutes

I don't like fish to be swamped with sauce. If you spread this citrus-spiked, spicy tomato sauce on to a plate and then set the cod on top of it, the two get along quite nicely and one does not dominate the other.

2 pieces frozen cod fillet	Pinch mild chilli powder
Juice of 2 limes	Salt and freshly ground pepper to
Juice of ½ small orange	taste
½ teaspoon cumin	Piquant Tomato Sauce (see below)
¼ teaspoon ground coriander	

1   Choose a plate that will hold the fillets in one layer, and will fit in your steamer arrangement, (see box, page 77.) Place the frozen cod fillets on the plate. Squeeze the citrus juices over the fish.

2   Mix the seasonings together and sprinkle them evenly over the fish. Leave to marinate while you make the tomato sauce (see below).

3   Fill the bottom of your wok with water and bring to the boil. (When boiling the water should not touch the bottom of the steamer rack.) Put the plate on the steamer rack. Cover and steam for approximately 10–15 minutes, or until the fish is just done.

4   Pour some of the sauce on to the centre of the plate. With a fish slice, lift one of the cod fillets, and centre it on the pool of sauce. Repeat with the second piece of fish. Serve at once.

✿♡✱🗋PIQUANT TOMATO SAUCE

Yields approx ¾ pt/400 ml

🕑 20 minutes

This is one of the many possible versions of my 'Instant Tomato Sauce' (see page 133). This particular quick tomato sauce is flavoured with an infusion of garlic, spring onions, orange juice and Mexican seasonings.

4–5 spring onions, trimmed and sliced	½ teaspoon ground cumin
	¼ teaspoon ground coriander
3–4 sun-dried tomatoes, chopped (use scissors) – optional	2 tablespoons orange juice
	6–8 fl oz/175–225 ml stock
1–2 cloves garlic, minced	1 box (1 lb 2 oz/500 g) passata
Pinch or two dried red chilli flakes	Freshly ground pepper to taste

1   Combine the onions, sun-dried tomatoes, garlic, chilli, cumin, coriander, orange juice and stock in a non-reactive frying pan. Cover and boil for 3–4 minutes. Uncover and

simmer until the mixture is almost dry and the onions and garlic are tender.

2 Stir in the passata and grind in some pepper. Simmer for 10–15 minutes.

♡ ## COUSCOUS SALAD WITH SMOKED MACKEREL AND ORANGES

Yields 2 pts/1.1 l

🕐 25 minutes

Packages of quick-cooking couscous are available in most large supermarkets. Preparation couldn't be easier; simply combine the couscous with boiling liquid and let stand for 10–15 minutes until the tiny grains of semolina have expanded and become tender. Couscous is delicious served hot with stews and sauces, or – as here – served cold as a main dish salad.

Couscous

Juice of ½ lime	seasoned stock
Juice of ½ orange	6 oz /175 g couscous
Finely grated zest of ½ lime	Salt and freshly ground pepper to
Finely grated zest of ½ orange	taste
Approx 6 fl oz/175 ml well-	

Dressing

2 tablespoons Balsamic vinegar	Several dashes each: Tabasco and
2 tablespoons fresh lime juice	Worcestershire sauce
2 tablespoons fresh orange juice	1 clove garlic, thoroughly crushed –
1 teaspoon Soy sauce	optional

Salad

1 large seedless orange, peeled of all skin and pith, and diced	3 oz/75 g tiny, shelled prawns
	2 tablespoons chopped parsley
1 fillet (approx 4 oz/110 g) smoked mackerel, flaked (be sure to remove any little bones)	4 spring onions, trimmed and sliced
	2 tablespoons shredded fresh mint

Garnish: Halved cherry tomatoes, small wedges of lemon, lime and orange.

1   Combine the lime juice, orange juice, zests and enough stock to bring the mixture to 8 fl oz/225 ml. Bring to the boil.
2   Combine the couscous, liquid and salt and pepper if it needs it. Let steep for 10–15 minutes until the liquid is absorbed and the grains are tender. Fluff with a fork.
3   Pour the dressing ingredients into a screw-top jar and shake well.
4   Mix together all the salad ingredients and stir in half of the dressing.
5   Toss the couscous, mackerel-prawn mixture and remaining dressing together. Pile on to a platter. Surround with the garnishes.

Vegetables

Anyone interested in good health and continued slimness should be committed to a lifelong love affair with vegetables. Eat a potato or two a day, along with lavish amounts of as many other vegetables as you can find, and you will be doing your health and waistline a great favour. Vegetables cooked the Slim Cuisine way with no added fat can be eaten singly or in combination in countless recipes: this chapter can only give an inkling of the possibilities. The recipes and techniques contained here should give you plenty of ideas for original dishes of your own.

I begin the chapter with a collection of therapeutic binges: hearty main-dish vegetable stews made – for convenience and speed – from frozen vegetables. If you want to lose some weight in a hurry, live off therapeutic binges (all you want to eat – that's the nature of a therapeutic binge), skimmed milk dairy products and lots of water for a week. You'll be astonished at how full and satisfied you will feel and how quickly the weight will fall away. A full list of skimmed milk dairy products can be found on page 14. The Therapeutic Binge Vegetable List follows. Eat the vegetables in any quantity, cooked according to Slim Cuisine principles (no added fat) or raw in salads with Slim Cuisine dressings (see index for dressing possibilities).

Quick Weight-Loss Therapeutic Binge Vegetable List

Use fresh or frozen. If you use frozen – read the label! Make sure *no added* fat has been used in the processing.

Artichokes (fresh or canned in brine, globe or Jerusalem)
Asparagus
Aubergines
Bean sprouts
Beetroot
Broccoli (calabrese)
Brussels sprouts
Cabbage (white and red)
Carrots
Cauliflower
Celeriac
Celery
Chicory
Courgettes
Cress
Cucumber
Endive
Fennel
Garlic
Greens (all kinds: beet greens, chard, etc.)

Herbs (fresh)
Kohlrabi
Leeks
Lettuce (all kinds)
Mange-tout
Marrow
Mooli
Mushrooms
Onions (all kinds)
Parsnips
Peppers (green, yellow, red)
Radishes
Runner beans
Spaghetti marrow
Spinach
Swedes
Sweetcorn cobs (tiny)
Tomatoes (fresh and canned)
Turnips
Watercress

Note: To measure out frozen vegetables pour them – still frozen – into a large measuring jug.

 THERAPEUTIC VEGETABLE STEW

Yields approx 2½ pts/1.4 l

🕐 25 minutes

This recipe and the three that follow are hearty, homely, deeply satisfying stews that are meant to comfort and sustain during both weight loss and weight maintenance. They are great served in big bowls and garnished with dollops of herb sauce: fromage frais mixed with chopped herbs. If you keep big bags of frozen vegetables in the freezer and tins of Italian tomatoes in the store cupboard, then you can have one of these therapeutic binges on the table in less than half an hour. There is no need to thaw the vegetables before you cook them. Simply pour them from their bag into a large measuring jug.

2 small tins (14 oz/400 g each) whole Italian tomatoes	cauliflower florets, frozen cut green beans, frozen sliced mixed
4 fl oz/110 ml stock or water	peppers, frozen diced swedes,
Juice and grated zest of 1 small lemon	frozen diced or sliced carrots, frozen courgettes (do not thaw
Pinch or two dried chilli flakes	any of the vegetables)
4–5 spring onions, trimmed and sliced thin	Salt and freshly ground pepper to taste
2 cloves garlic, crushed	3 tablespoons snipped chives
3–4 sun-dried tomatoes, diced (use scissors) – optional	4 tablespoons shredded basil or mint leaves
½–¾ pt/300–400 ml each: frozen	4 tablespoons chopped parsley

1   Drain the tomatoes very well and save the juice. With your fingers, break up the tomatoes. Set them aside.
2   Put ½ pt/300 ml of the tomato juice, the stock or water, half the lemon juice and zest, the chillies, spring onions, garlic and sun-dried tomatoes in a heavy bottomed pot. Cover and bring to the boil. Boil for 7 minutes. Uncover and simmer briskly until the garlic has mellowed somewhat and the liquid has reduced and thickened.
3   Stir in all the frozen vegetables, the tomatoes and season with salt and pepper. Cook, partially covered, stirring occasionally for 10 minutes. Add the remaining lemon juice and zest and the fresh herbs and cook briskly, uncovered, stirring occasionally, until the vegetables are tender and bathed in a thick sauce (the dish should not be too soupy). Taste and adjust the seasonings.

✿♡❁ THERAPEUTIC VEGETABLE CURRY

Yields approximately 2½ pts/1.4 l

🕐 25 minutes

All these therapeutic stews utilize the same basic method, but different spicing (and different combinations of vegetables) give them different character. Serve this curry version garnished with fromage frais mixed with shredded fresh mint and coriander leaves.

2 small tins (14 oz/400 g each)
whole Italian tomatoes
4 fl oz/110 ml stock or water
Juice and grated zest of 1 lime
4–5 spring onions, trimmed and
sliced thin
2 cloves garlic, crushed
3–4 sun-dried tomatoes, diced (use
scissors) – optional
Generous pinch or two crushed
dried chillies
Pinch ground cloves
⅛ teaspoon ground allspice
1 teaspoon each: ground ginger,
ground turmeric, ground
coriander, ground cinnamon,
ground cumin
½ teaspoon light brown sugar
½–¾ pt/300–400 ml each: frozen
sliced peppers, frozen sliced
carrots, frozen cut cabbage,
frozen diced swedes, frozen cut
green beans, frozen sliced
courgettes
Salt and freshly ground pepper to
taste
4 tablespoons shredded fresh mint
2–3 tablespoons chopped fresh
coriander

1   Drain the tomatoes very well and save the juices. With your fingers, break up the tomatoes. Set them aside.

2   Put ½ pt/300 ml of the tomato juice, the stock or water, half the lime juice and zest, the spring onions, garlic, sun-dried tomatoes, chillies, ground spices and brown sugar into a heavy bottomed pot. Cover and bring to the boil. Reduce the heat somewhat and simmer for 5 minutes. Uncover and simmer, stirring occasionally, until the garlic is tender and the liquid has reduced and thickened.

3   Stir in all the frozen vegetables, along with the tomatoes and season with salt and pepper. Cook, partially covered, stirring occasionally, for 10 minutes. Add the remaining lime juice and zest and simmer uncovered, stirring occasionally until the vegetables are tender and bathed in a thick, not too soupy, sauce. Mix in the fresh herbs, taste and adjust seasonings.

THERAPEUTIC VEGETABLE CHILLI

Yields approx 2½ pt/1.4 l

🕐 25 minutes

Serve the chilli version of the Therapeutic Vegetable Stew with a garnish of fromage frais mixed with chopped fresh coriander leaves.

2 small tins (14 oz/400 g each) whole Italian tomatoes
6 fl oz/175 ml stock or water
Juice and grated rind of 1 lime
4–5 spring onions, trimmed and sliced
2 cloves garlic, crushed
3–4 sun-dried tomatoes, diced (use scissors) – optional
1–2 tablespoons mild chilli powder
1 tablespoon ground cumin
½ teaspoon ground cinnamon
½–¾ pt/300–400 ml each: frozen cauliflower florets, frozen broccoli florets, frozen sliced peppers, frozen diced swedes, frozen sliced courgettes, frozen sliced or diced carrots
Salt and freshly ground pepper to taste
1–2 tablespoons chopped fresh oregano
1–2 tablespoons chopped fresh coriander – optional

1   Drain the tomatoes very well and save the juice. With your fingers, break up the tomatoes. Set them aside.
2   Put ½ pt/300 ml of the tomato juice, the stock or water, half the lime rind and juice, the spring onions, garlic, sun-dried tomatoes and spices into a heavy bottomed pot. Cover and bring to the boil. Boil for 7 minutes. Uncover and simmer briskly until the garlic is tender and the liquid has reduced and thickened.
3   Stir in all the frozen vegetables, the tomatoes and season with salt and pepper. Cook, partially covered, stirring occasionally for 10 minutes. Add the remaining lime juice and zest and simmer uncovered, stirring occasionally, until the vegetables are tender and bathed in a thick sauce. Taste and adjust seasonings.

 THERAPEUTIC VEGETABLE PARIKASH

THERAPEUTIC VEGETABLE PAPRIKASH

Yields approx 2½ pts/1.4 l

25 minutes

Recently there has been a vogue for exotic food: Mexican; Cajun; Tex-Mex; Italian; Chinese (from Cantonese to Hunanese and beyond); Japanese. Will Hungarian ever become the flavour of the year? I love the flavour principles of Hungarian food and often use them, but the lard – needless to say – I dispense with altogether. Serve the paprikash with a garnish of fromage frais mixed with marjoram or dill.

2 small tins (14 oz/400 g each)
whole Italian tomatoes
4 fl oz/110 ml stock or water
Juice and grated zest of ½ lemon
4–5 spring onions, trimmed and
sliced thin
2 cloves garlic, crushed
3–4 sun-dried tomatoes, diced (use
scissors) – optional
1 tablespoon paprika or paprika
paste

1 tablespoon caraway seeds
Pinch dried chillies
½–¾ pt/300–400 ml each: frozen
cauliflower florets, frozen sliced
mixed peppers, frozen diced
swedes, frozen diced or sliced
carrots, frozen cut green beans,
frozen sliced courgettes (do not
thaw)
Salt and freshly ground pepper to
taste

1   Drain the tomatoes very well and save the juices. With your fingers break up the tomatoes. Set them aside.

2   Put ½ pt/300 ml of the tomato juice, the stock or water, lemon juice and zest, spring onions, garlic, sun-dried tomatoes, paprika, caraway seeds and chillies into a heavy bottomed pot. Cover and bring to the boil. Reduce the heat somewhat and simmer for 5 minutes. Uncover and simmer, stirring occasionally, until the garlic is tender and the liquid has reduced and thickened.

3   Add all the frozen vegetables, along with the tomatoes and season with salt and pepper. Cook, partially covered, stirring intermittently, for 10 minutes. Uncover and cook, stirring occasionally, until the vegetables are tender and bathed in a thick sauce. Taste and adjust seasonings.

PIPERADE FLAN

Yields 1 11 inch/28 cm flan

Tomato–Pepper Conserve: 20 minutes (make it while the oven preheats)
Flan: 30 minutes ·

This flan and the three that follow are meant to be served as either side dishes or vegetarian main dishes. Each contains 3 egg whites and one whole egg. These flans are a sort of cross between quiche and Spanish tortilla or Italian frittata. They are quite easy to make – I'm sure that you will think up lots of new fillings for them.

Batter mix:

8 fl oz/225 ml skimmed milk	3 egg whites
4 tablespoons skimmed milk powder	1 whole egg
Salt and freshly ground pepper to taste	
2½ oz/60 g self-raising white flour	One recipe of Tomato-Pepper Conserve (see page 102)

1 Preheat the oven to 350°F, 180°C, Gas Mark 4.
2 Combine the batter ingredients in a blender and process until smooth and well mixed.
3 Pour 5 fl oz/150 ml of the batter into an 11–12-inch/28–30.5-cm flan dish. Bake for 4 minutes.
4 Spread the conserve evenly over the base. Pour the remaining batter over the conserve. Bake in the preheated oven for 20–25 minutes until puffed, browned and firm (a cake tester will emerge clean).

MUSHROOM FLAN

Yields 1 11-inch/28-cm flan

Mushrooms: 15 minutes (prepare them while the oven preheats)
Flan: 30 minutes

These flans are so *easy*: simply prepare a quick, savoury vegetable mixture, whizz together some milk, flour and egg in a blender to form a batter and bake it all in a flan tin for half an hour. I find that baking some of the batter in the tin, before adding the vegetables and remaining batter, forms a nice, tender base for the flan. The flans are good served hot, cold or at room temperature. This variation overflows with mushrooms that have been simmered with a little bit of lean back bacon for its smoky flavour and Dijon mustard for its pizzazz. Leave out the bacon by all means if you do not eat pork.

Batter mix:

8 fl oz/225 ml skimmed milk	3 egg whites
4 tablespoons skimmed milk powder	1 whole egg
Salt and freshly ground pepper to taste	2 tablespoons Parmesan cheese
2½ oz/60 g white self-raising flour	1 recipe, Mushrooms on toast (see page 105)

1   Preheat the oven to 350°F, 180°C, Gas Mark 4.
2   Combine the batter ingredients thoroughly in a blender. Process until smooth and well mixed. Pulse in the Parmesan cheese.
3   Pour 5 fl oz/150 ml of the batter into an 11–12-inch/28–30.5-cm flan dish. Bake for 4 minutes.
4   Spread the mushrooms evenly over the base. Pour the remaining batter over the mushrooms. Bake in the preheated oven for 25–30 minutes until puffed, firm and browned (a cake tester will emerge clean).

SPINACH FLAN

Yields 1 12-inch/30.5-cm flan

⊕ 35 minutes

The spinach filling in this flan is flavoured in a Middle-Eastern style: cinnamon, ground coriander, sultanas and lemon. It is equally good hot or cold.

Filling:

Yields 1 pt/570 ml filling

6 spring onions, trimmed and sliced	Juice and grated zest of ½ lemon
2 cloves garlic, crushed	1½ lb/700 g frozen chopped
2 tablespoons sultanas	spinach, thawed, drained and
Pinch cayenne pepper	squeezed dry
¼ teaspoon ground cinnamon	Salt and freshly ground pepper to
½ teaspoon ground coriander	taste
½ pt/300 ml stock	

Batter mix:

8 fl oz/225 ml skimmed milk	2½ oz/60 g white self-raising flour
4 tablespoons skimmed milk powder	3 egg whites
Salt and freshly ground pepper to	1 whole egg
taste	

1 Preheat the oven to 350°F, 180°C, Gas Mark 4.
2 Meanwhile combine the onions, garlic, sultanas, spices, stock, lemon juice and zest in a heavy bottomed, non-reactive frying pan. Cover and boil for 5 minutes.
3 Uncover. Stir in the spinach and season with salt and pepper. Cook and stir for a few minutes over a very low heat to coat the spinach thoroughly with the onion mixture and to blend the flavours. Taste and adjust seasonings, adding salt, pepper, lemon juice or spices as needed.
4 Combine the batter ingredients in a blender. Process until smooth and well mixed. Pour 5 fl oz/150 ml of the batter into an 11–12-inch/28–30.5-cm flan dish. Bake for 4 minutes.
5 Spread the spinach mixture evenly over the base. Pour the remaining batter over the spinach. Bake in the preheated oven for 20–25 minutes until puffed, firm and browned (a cake tester will emerge clean).

COURGETTE FLAN

Yields 1 12-inch/30.5-cm flan

45 minutes

Courgette strips, sun-dried tomatoes and basil give this flan a Mediterranean profile. The filling can easily be served on its own as a vegetable side dish. The flan would make a happy addition to a gala Sunday Brunch menu.

Filling
Yields 1 pt/570 ml filling

4 sun-dried tomatoes, chopped (use scissors) – optional	5-cm long, and ½-inch/1-cm wide
6 spring onions, trimmed and sliced thin	Juice of ½ lemon
3 cloves garlic, crushed	Salt and freshly ground pepper to taste
½ pt/300 ml stock	2 tablespoons each: chopped parsley and shredded basil
1 lb/450 g courgettes, trimmed and cut into strips about 2-inch/	

Batter mix

8 fl oz/225 ml skimmed milk	2½ oz/60 g white self-raising flour
4 tablespoons skimmed milk powder	3 egg whites
Salt and freshly ground pepper to taste	1 whole egg

1   Preheat the oven to 350°F, 180°C, Gas Mark 4.
2   Meanwhile, combine the sun-dried tomatoes, spring onions, garlic and 4 fl oz/110 ml stock in a heavy bottomed frying pan. Cover and boil for 5 minutes. Uncover and cook briskly until the liquid is greatly reduced and syrupy.
3   Stir in the courgettes, remaining stock and lemon juice. Season with salt and pepper. Add the herbs. Cook, stirring, over a high heat, until the courgettes are crisp-tender and the liquid is almost gone. Set aside.
4   Combine the batter ingredients in a blender. Process until smooth and well mixed. Pour 5 fl oz/150 ml of the batter into an 11–12-inch/28–30.5-cm flan dish. Bake for 4 minutes.
5   Spread the courgette mixture evenly over the base. Pour the remaining batter over the courgettes. Bake in the preheated oven for 20–25 minutes until puffed, firm and browned (a cake tester will emerge clean).

CAULIFLOWER CHEESE

Yields 2 pts/1.1 l

🕐 20 minutes

Cauliflower nestled in a creamy, not too bland, sauce under a browned and bubbly crust of melted cheese is spectacular food. At the end of a disastrous day there are few dishes that equal it in comfort power. My version is *fast* and it uses my new Slim Cuisine Cheese Sauce. Don't bother telling people what a great nutritional profile this recipe has, what with its lovely protein and calcium, and its low-fat level – just serve it forth and let them luxuriate.

2 large heads cauliflower, trimmed and broken into florets	Approx ½ pt/300 ml stock
6 spring onions, trimmed and sliced	2–3 tablespoons dry vermouth
4–5 sun-dried tomatoes, diced with scissors – optional	Approx ¾ pt/400 ml Cheese Sauce (see page 137)
1–2 cloves garlic, crushed	2–3 tablespoons grated Parmesan cheese
Pinch or two crushed dried chillies	

1   Preheat the grill.
2   Put the cauliflower into a steamer over boiling water. Steam until tender but not overcooked. Or cook in a microwave.
3   Spread the cauliflower in a 10-inch/25.5-cm square, 2-inch/5-cm deep baking dish or gratin dish. Set aside.
4   Meanwhile combine the spring onions, sun-dried tomatoes,

A mouthwatering barbecue with Mexican flair: clockwise from the grill: Fajitas (spice-rubbed, grilled skirt steak); spicy baked beans; mock guacamole (Green pea dip); tomato-pepper salsa; and fruit-ricotta brulée.

A birthday party for Teddy and friends indulges the sweet tooth
in a healthy way: clockwise from bottom left: Swiss roll filled
with sweetened quark and raspberries; chocolate bread and
chocolate 'butter'; chocolate stir-crazy cake filled with whipped,
sweetened quark and iced with chocolate 'butter'; pizza; fruit
bread; and tomato sandwiches on ham and cheese bread.

garlic, dried chillies, stock and vermouth in a heavy bottomed, non-reactive frying pan. Cover and boil for 5 minutes. Uncover and simmer until the garlic and onions are tender and the liquid is almost gone – the mixture will be syrupy. Stir this mixture into the cheese sauce.

5   If the cheese sauce is not freshly made and hot, warm it according to the directions on page 137. Pour and spread the sauce evenly over the cauliflower. Sprinkle with the grated Parmesan.

6   Grill a few inches from the heat for 3–5 minutes, until speckled with brown and beginning to bubble. Serve at once.

♡   Omit the cheese (you'll have to call it Cauliflower in Cream Sauce).

AUBERGINE GRATIN

Serves 4

⏱ 25 minutes

The original of this recipe (I used to make it in my Fat-Cuisine days) is shockingly high in fat. The aubergine slices were pan-fried in olive oil (they soak up oil like sponges), the sauce was made with butter and half-cream, and – if I remember correctly – the cheese topping was a generous layer of fontina cheese – not exactly one of your low-fat dishes. The Slim Cuisine version, obviously, contains only a very small fraction of the fat and Calories of the original, but there is *no compromise*. This version is better (I wouldn't lie to you). It has creaminess without fattiness, it has meltingly tender aubergine slices, it has sweet and mellow garlic, it has the deep taste of sun-dried tomatoes. The melted-cheese topping is sumptuously toasted-cheesy without being excessive . . . It's time for me to *shut up*, and for you to go into the kitchen to cook this extravaganza. You'll see that I am not exaggerating in the least.

---

2 aubergines (approx ½ lb/225 g each), sliced approx ¼-inch/ 0.5-cm thick	Pinch or two crushed dried chillies
	Approx ½ pt-300 ml stock
	2–3 tablespoons dry vermouth
6 spring onions, trimmed and sliced	Approx ¾ pt/400 ml Cheese Sauce
4–5 sun-dried tomatoes, diced with scissors – optional	(see page 137)
	2–3 tablespoons grated Parmesan cheese
1–2 cloves garlic, crushed	

---

1   Preheat the grill.
2   Arrange the aubergine slices in one layer on a non-stick baking sheet. Grill on one side only, until toasted and tender (approx 5–7 minutes).

3   Spread the aubergine slices in one layer in a 10-inch/25.5-cm square, 2-inch/5-cm deep baking dish or gratin dish. Set aside.

4   Meanwhile combine the spring onions, sun-dried tomatoes, garlic, dried chillies, stock and vermouth in a heavy bottomed, non-reactive frying pan. Cover and boil for 5 minutes. Uncover and simmer until the garlic and onions are tender and the liquid is almost gone – the mixture will be syrupy. Spread this mixture evenly over the aubergine, using a rubber spatula to scrape out every bit.

5   If the cheese sauce is not freshly made and hot, warm it according to the directions on page 137. Pour the sauce evenly over the aubergine. Sprinkle with the grated Parmesan.

6   Grill, a few inches the heat for 3–5 minutes, until speckled with brown and beginning to bubble. Serve at once.

♡   Omit the Parmesan cheese, and use White Sauce (see page 135) in place of Cheese Sauce.

MACARONI CHEESE

🕐 20 minutes

Make the sauce while the pasta cooks and you have a fast meal indeed. Is there anyone out there who doesn't like Macaroni Cheese? There are some nursery dishes that never grow old.

1 lb/450 g large, tubular macaroni (penne or rigatoni)	Mustardy White Sauce (see pages 137 and 138)
1 pt/570 ml Cheese Sauce or	3–4 tablespoons Parmesan Cheese

1   Fill a large pot with salted water and bring to the boil.
2   Preheat the grill. Set a colander in the sink.
3   When the water boils stir in the pasta. Cook, stirring occasionally, until the pasta is al dente (cooked but not mushy).
4   While the pasta is cooking, make the sauce (see pages 137 or 138).
5   Drain the pasta in the colander. Pour it into a 10-inch/25.5-cm square, 2-inch/5-cm deep baking dish, or an oval gratin dish. Pour the sauce over the pasta and – with two large spoons – toss it all together. The pasta should be well coated with the sauce. Sprinkle on the cheese.
6   Grill, not too close to the heat, for about 5 minutes, or until the cheese is melted, the sauce is bubbly and the top layer of pasta is lightly speckled with brown. Serve at once.

♡ Make Macaroni in Cream Sauce: substitute White Sauce (see page 135) or Mustardy White Sauce (see page 138) for the Cheese Sauce. Do not sprinkle the top with grated cheese.

BREAD AND SWEETCORN PIE

Yields 1–10-inch/25.5-cm pie

🕐 50 minutes

Savoury bread puddings make pleasing, economical and easy family meals. Put the stale bread cubes in a deep pie pan, bathe them in an egg (1 yolk, 3 whites) custard studded with kernels of sweetcorn and cubes of mozzarella, season with chillies and bake until the pie puffs up like a soufflé and emits wafts of toasted cheese . . . This is what comfort food is all about.

1 can (10½ oz/285 g) creamed corn	1 can (4 oz/110 g) green chillies,
1 whole egg	drained and chopped
3 egg whites	5 spring onions, trimmed, sliced
4 fl oz/110 ml skimmed milk	thin and sautéed in a bit of stock
Salt and freshly ground pepper to	until tender
taste	Pinch or two each: cayenne pepper
6 oz/175 g stale bread, cubed	and cumin
1 large can (approx 12 oz/350 g)	4 oz/110 g mozzarella cheese, cubed
drained corn kernels	1–2 tablespoons Parmesan cheese

1 Preheat the oven to 350°F, 180°C, Gas Mark 4.
2 Meanwhile in a large bowl, beat together the creamed corn, whole egg and egg whites. Stir in all the remaining ingredients except the Parmesan cheese. Use 2 spoons to toss the mixture together very well so that the bread absorbs the liquid.
3 Pour the mixture into a 10-inch/25.5-cm round, 2-inches/5-cm deep glass pie dish (or use a square casserole or a gratin dish). Bake for 30–40 minutes. Sprinkle on the cheese approximately 5–10 minutes before the pie is done. When it is puffy, browned, and a knife inserted near the centre tests clean, remove from the oven and allow to stand on a rack for 5–10 minutes. To serve, cut into wedges.

Sweetcorn Memories

For years, I've been a purist about fresh sweetcorn. My sweetcorn sensibilities were honed during summers spent on the coast of Maine. Local farmers would post daily harvest times on a board at their farm stands. My husband was often one of the vegetable-mad crowd waiting at the appointed moment: the car's motor was running, the farmer and his helpers rushed the just-picked ears to eagerly waiting arms, money hastily changed hands, and whoosh! Everyone broke the speed limit, burning up the tarmac back to their kitchens. In my kitchen, a gargantuan pot boiled on the stove (it did double duty each summer: sometimes lobster, sometimes ears of corn). I rushed to the car to help carry the ears – we both ran into the kitchen, shucking the ears as we ran – splash, the corn spent just a few minutes in the boiling water before it was yanked out, salted, peppered, slathered with butter (yes, these were the old Fat-Cuisine days) and devoured. Inevitably, the feast of corn would be followed by overflowing bowls of just-picked blueberries. Oh, those halcyon summer Maine days: days of corn, berries, new potatoes, lobster . . . Because of the vivid taste memories of those farm stand-cabin sweetcorn runs, I *never* buy store-bought fresh sweetcorn on the cob. Corn lovers have always agreed that canned kernel corn is good – the kernels take quite well to the canning process. It's not that canned corn is a substitute for the real thing – it is, rather, a quite acceptable vegetable in itself, and invaluable for casseroles, soups, corn breads and so on. Frozen corn kernels, too, it was generally agreed were pretty good: since the sugars in fresh corn start to turn to starch as soon as the ears are picked (hence the mad summer rush from stalk to boiling water to plate), it makes sense to have freezing plants on or near the farms, so that corn can be picked, processed and frozen as quickly as possible. (Frozen corn is much preferable to 'fresh' ears that have been packed, shipped, left on docks, and set on supermarket shelves . . . days [even *weeks*] pass between stalk and boiling water.) So no one had any problems using the canned and frozen product out of season. It didn't deliver the toothsome, bursting sweetness and ecstasy of a farm-to-pot run, but it was a good staple to use between seasons.

Imagine my surprise, when – one day – looking for a quick snack on a busy day, I pulled some frozen sweetcorn (bred for extra sweetness) out of the freezer, dumped some into a bowl with no added salt, or liquid or anything else, covered it with cling film and set it in the microwave for 5 minutes. While it cooked, I pottered around in another part of the house. When I returned to the kitchen about 10 minutes later, it hit me: the kitchen was fragrant with the perfume of Maine summertimes. Of course, the drama and adrenalin of break the speed limit, shuck-as-you-run, heave it into the pot, gnaw-it-off-the-cob was missing but the smell! The taste! Pure summer-sweet, maize essence. Convenience food? Who would have believed that such a thing could be possible?

 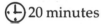

CAULIFLOWER BRAISED IN RED WINE

Yields ¾ pt/400 ml

🕐 20 minutes

Cauliflower braised to tenderness in red wine and stock takes on a lovely pale purply colour. The alcohol (and the alcohol Calories) cook away as the sauce simmers, so the finished dish will not cause anyone to become inebriated.

---

6 fl oz/175 ml stock	2 fl oz/50 ml dry red wine
1 onion, chopped fine	Salt and freshly ground pepper to
3 cloves garlic, crushed	taste
1 large cauliflower, trimmed and	
broken into florets	

---

1   Combine 4 fl oz/110 ml stock, onion and garlic in a frying pan. Cover and bring to the boil for 3–4 minutes. Uncover and simmer until the onions are tender and amber, and the liquid has almost cooked away.
2   Add the cauliflower and pour in the remaining stock and wine. Cover and simmer gently for 10–12 minutes. Raise the heat and cook briskly, stirring, until the wine has evaporated, and the cauliflower is a beautiful purple colour. Season to taste.

🐻♡🥕 TOMATO-PEPPER CONSERVE

Yields ½ pt/300 ml

🕐 20 minutes

It doesn't take long to peel a pepper (see page 125). I fervently believe that the peeling makes a big difference to the quality and digestibility of the finished dish. But when all is said and done, you are the one who has to decide how much kitchen work you want to bear; if it's too much trouble, you're free to skip the peeling. This conserve is used in the Piperade Flan (see page 92) and the Piperade Pork Steaks (see page 56), but it also makes a delightful sandwich filling, garnish for poached chicken breasts or vegetable side dish.

---

1 large onion, cut in half and sliced into thin half-moons
½ pt/300 ml stock
2 cloves garlic, minced
1 large red pepper, cut into its natural sections, peeled and then cut into strips

8 fl oz/225 ml (approx ½ of a 14 oz/400 g can) chopped tomatoes
Salt and freshly ground pepper to taste
1 tablespoon chopped fresh parsley

---

1   Combine the onion slices and 6 fl oz/175 ml stock in a heavy bottomed frying pan. Cover and boil for 7–10 minutes. Uncover and simmer briskly until the liquid has almost gone, and the onions are sticking to the bottom of the pan and browning. Pour in the remaining stock and stir in the garlic and pepper slices. Simmer, stirring occasionally, and scraping up the browned bits with your wooden spoon. Stir in the tomatoes, salt, pepper and parsley. Simmer briskly until the peppers are tender and the mixture is very thick.

COURGETTES WITH TOMATO AND BASIL

Yields 1½ pts/900 ml

🕐 20 minutes

The microwave does an outstanding job of cooking fresh vegetables. Courgettes emerge from the microwave with a bursting freshness and just the right compromise between 'crisp' and 'tender'. The tomatoes cook down to a light, sauce-like consistency. An advantage of using a microwave is that it does a good job of preserving the nutrients in vegetables as well.

3–4 fresh, ripe tomatoes, peeled and seeded and sliced into ½-inch/ 1-cm strips
2 cloves garlic, crushed – optional
1½ lb/700 g courgettes, trimmed

and sliced ½-inch/1-cm thick
Salt and freshly ground pepper to taste
2 tablespoons shredded basil or mint leaves

---

1   Combine the tomatoes, and garlic if using, in a 10-inch/25.5-cm square, 2-inch/5-cm deep microwave safe dish.
2   Toss in the courgettes. Cover tightly with cling film and microwave for 5 minutes. Uncover, stir, re-cover and cook for 3 minutes more. Season with salt and pepper, stir in the basil and allow to stand for 5 minutes.

SUNCHOKES (JERUSALEM ARTICHOKES) WITH SPRING ONIONS

Yields approx 1¼ pt/700 ml

🕐 25 minutes

Jerusalem artichokes are small, knobbly roots with a pleasantly starchy quality. They look nothing like globe artichokes and are not botanically related to globe artichokes, but do have a slight similarity of flavour. Jerusalem artichokes can be cooked like potatoes: scrub and peel them, boil or steam them and then mash (they are wonderful half and half with mashed potatoes); slice them (unpeeled) and bake in a gratin; or – as in this recipe – slice them and stir 'fry' them in stock with spring onions. I add no seasonings other than salt and pepper, because the simple earthy flavour of the sunchokes and the fresh savour of the spring onions need no embellishment.

20 spring onions	8 fl oz/225 ml stock
1 lb/450 g Jerusalem artichokes (sunchokes)	Salt and freshly ground pepper to taste

1   Wash, trim and cut onions crosswise into four pieces each.
2   Scrub the artichokes and thinly slice. (There is no need to peel them.)
3   Pour the stock into a heavy bottomed frying pan. Bring to the boil. Toss in the artichokes. Sauté the artichokes in the briskly simmering stock for approximately 10 minutes. Add the onions and continue to sauté until both the artichokes and the spring onions are tender and the liquid has almost cooked away.
4   Season to taste and serve at once.

 SPICED CARROTS

Yields 1 pt/570 ml

⏱ 25 minutes

If you were really pressed for time, you could make this spicy, lemony, braised carrot dish with frozen sliced carrots, but fresh carrots really have a better texture. With a trusty swivel-bladed peeler, carrot peeling is a fairly swift exercise.

1 pt/570 ml stock	Pinch sugar
4 cloves garlic, crushed	Juice of 1 small lemon
½ teaspoon ground cumin	1 lb/450 g carrots, peeled and sliced
Pinch ground cinnamon	Salt and freshly ground pepper to
Pinch cayenne pepper	taste

1   Combine all the ingredients except the carrots, salt and pepper in a non-reactive frying pan. Cover and boil for 3–4 minutes.
2   Stir in the carrots and season to taste. Cook, uncovered, stirring and tossing, until the carrots are tender and glazed. Serve at once.

MUSHROOMS ON TOAST

Yields ¾ pt/400 ml

🕐 15 minutes

The 'Holy Trinity' of Slim Cuisine mushroom cookery consists of stock, dry wine and Soy or Teriyaki sauce. If you enhance that trinity with a bit of lean back bacon (for its smokiness), Dijon mustard (for its piquancy) and tarragon (for its brilliant affinity with mushrooms), then spread the cooked mushrooms on a slice of the best toast, you have a very special version of a fast-food classic. The mushroom mixture can also be used as a vegetable side dish or as the filling in the Mushroom Flan on page 93 or the stuffed pork loin steaks on page 58.

---

1 lb/450 g assorted mushrooms, quartered	*10–12 spring onions, trimmed and sliced*
4 fl oz/110 ml stock	*2 teaspoons Dijon mustard*
4 fl oz/110 ml dry vermouth	*1 teaspoon dried tarragon*
Several dashes Teriyaki sauce	*Freshly ground pepper to taste*
2 slices smoked back bacon, trimmed of all fat and diced	

---

1   Combine the mushrooms, stock, vermouth, Teriyaki sauce, bacon and spring onions in a heavy bottomed, non reactive frying pan. Cook briskly until the liquid has greatly reduced. Stir occasionally.
2   Add the mustard, tarragon and pepper. Continue cooking for 3–4 minutes, until the mushrooms are tender and bathed in a mustardy sauce.
3   Serve on hot toast.

 Omit the bacon, and serve the mushrooms without toast.

GINGERED MUSHROOMS

Yields 1 pt/570 ml

⏱ 15 minutes

Crystallized ginger (it's like spicy, ginger-flavoured, hard gum) is a great store-cupboard staple. A slivered lump of crystallized ginger can be slipped into savoury recipes to give an unexpected gingery bite. Here, a few lumps are minced with scissors and slipped in with the mushroom 'trinity' – stock, dry wine and Teriyaki sauce – along with a couple of dashes of Balsamic vinegar as well. The mushrooms take on a gingery, sweet-and-sour edge that is most pleasing.

1 lb/450 g small button mushrooms	*ginger, finely chopped (use*
6 fl oz/175 ml stock	*scissors)*
2 fl oz/50 ml dry sherry	*Dash or two Teriyaki sauce*
2–3 small lumps of crystallized	*Dash or two Balsamic vinegar*

1   Combine all the ingredients in a heavy bottomed, non-reactive frying pan. Bring to the boil. Cook, stirring occasionally. The mushrooms will render quite a bit of juice. Continue cooking, stirring occasionally, until the mushrooms are tender and the liquid has almost gone. Do not allow them to stick or burn. Serve hot or at room temperature. Store in the refrigerator.

🧸 ♡ Omit crystallized ginger.

MUSHROOMS *EN PAPILLOTE*

⏱ 25 minutes

En papillote is a classic manner of cookery that wraps food in a 'paper bag', usually parchment paper or greaseproof paper. In these modern times, the paper bag is sometimes – as here – a folder of aluminium foil. Large mushrooms bathed in garlic, parsley, sherry, Soy sauce and orange juice and rind are folded inside a foil envelope and baked in a hot oven until they become imbued with the fragrant ingredients. Serve these juicy, saucy, flavourful beauties on toast so that the bread soaks up all the gorgeous juices.

Field mushrooms, stems removed	*Dry sherry*
Chopped parsley	*Fresh orange juice*
Grated orange rind	*Soy or Teriyaki sauce*
Minced fresh garlic	*Freshly ground black pepper*

1   Preheat the oven to 400°F, 200°C, Gas Mark 6.
2   For every two servings, tear a piece of foil large enough to enfold 2 large mushrooms (in one layer). Place the foil, shiny side up, on your work surface. Place the mushrooms on the foil, gill-sides up. Scatter on approximately 1 tablespoon chopped parsley, a bit of orange rind and 1 clove minced garlic, sprinkle on 1 tablespoon of dry sherry and 1 of orange juice, shake on a modest dash or two of Soy or Teriyaki sauce, and grind on some pepper to taste.
3   Fold over the foil and seal all around, so that the mushrooms are in a roomy, well-sealed pouch. Bake directly on the oven shelf for 20 minutes. The mushrooms are delicious served on pieces of toast (use the best bread you can find) or in a split, freshly baked, quick baguette (see page 163). Saturate each piece of bread with the juices and set mushroom on top. Eat with a knife and fork.

♡ ⵷ ❄ ☐   SPICY 'BAKED' BEANS

Yields 1½ pts/900 ml

🕐 25 minutes

These beans are not really *baked* – they are prepared quickly in a frying pan with canned beans, tomato passata and a bunch of bean-enhancing seasonings. Why, why, why would you want to open a can of ordinary baked beans for supper, when you can have a bean feast like this in less than half an hour?

---

12 spring onions, trimmed and
  sliced
3–4 cloves garlic, cut into chunks
3–4 sun-dried tomatoes, chopped
  (use scissors) – optional
½ pt/300 ml stock
3–4 fl oz/75–110 ml dry white
  vermouth
Generous pinch or two each:
  ground cumin and crushed
  dried chillies
2 cans (15¾ oz/430 g each) beans
(use black-eyed beans and kidney
  beans, or Borlotti beans and
  cannellini beans), rinsed and
  drained very well

1 pt/570 ml passata (sieved
  tomatoes), or 1 can (14 oz/
  400 g) chopped tomatoes
  whizzed smooth in the blender,
  mixed with 3 tablespoons
  tomato purée
Salt and freshly ground pepper to
  taste
2 tablespoons chopped fresh parsley
1–2 tablespoons chopped fresh
  coriander, or shredded mint, or
  shredded basil
Juice of ½ lime

---

1   Combine the onions, garlic, sun-dried tomatoes, stock, vermouth, cumin and chillies in a heavy pan. Cover and boil for 5–7 minutes. Uncover and simmer briskly, stirring occasionally, until the liquid is cooked down and syrupy, and the garlic is meltingly tender.

3   Add the beans and stir to coat them with the spring onion–spice mixture. Mix in the passata and season to taste. Simmer uncovered for 15 minutes.

3   Stir in the chopped herbs and lime juice. Serve at once, or – for a slightly Mexican effect – mash (with a potato masher right in the pan) about a quarter of the beans and then stir.

A Toast to the Noble Bean

'Something on Toast' is one solution to the perennial problem of what to serve for tea at the end of a particularly busy day. That 'something' is usually canned baked beans although I have heard rumours that canned spaghetti is sometimes heaped on to a slice of toast and passed off as a decent meal. The very idea of canned spaghetti is bad enough, but on *toast*? Give me a break! Baked beans, though – what a good idea. Make it a slice of good brown bread, topped with a heap of home-made baked beans, and you have a simple, healthy and delicious feast that calms frazzled nerves and soothes deep hungers. You can make your own delicious baked beans almost instantly by starting with tinned beans: cannellini, black-eyed, red kidney, Borlotti, whatever you like. I think a mixure of two or more types make a really interesting dish. The toast can be a slice of your own home-made bread (see pages 159–63) or a slice of excellent quality bakery wholemeal bread. Of course, the baked beans – when prepared from canned beans – are not *really* baked; to bake them you would need to start with dried beans, soak them overnight, drain them and then bake them for hours. But still – what a comforting delicious instant meal you get for such a paltry investment of time.

❋ ⯑ OLD-FASHIONED 'BAKED' BEANS

Yields 1¼ pts/700 ml

🕐 30 minutes

I lived for a while in Cambridge, Massachusetts, right across the river from Boston, otherwise known as 'Bean Town'. Boston Baked Beans – what a treat. In that part of America, beans are a way of life along with scrod, codfish cakes, grapenuts, Indian pudding and the Red Sox. Bean Town Bean eaters can make their own (it takes hours and there are as many theories about the *proper* way to make them as there are about Bouillabaisse in Marseilles, or Cassoulet in the Languedoc) or they can go to the supermarket. Here, we have only 1–2 varieties of canned baked beans to choose from, Bostonians have dozens. There's the pea bean, the kidney bean or the navy bean, there's salt pork, bacon or vegetarian, there's brick oven or (presumably) non-brick oven, there's molasses or brown sugar or corn syrup. If you were in the mood for a baked-bean supper, the choices could drive you mad. If you want a taste of Boston for your supper one night, choose your beans and use my recipe: it's a little jazzed up and it's *fast*, but it has a basically Boston profile.

---

2 well-trimmed slices smoked
    bacon, diced (leave it out if you
    don't eat pork)
2 cloves garlic, crushed
1 small onion, minced
2–3 sun-dried tomatoes, minced
    (use scissors) – optional
Pinch chilli flakes
½ pt/300 ml stock
1 can (15¾ oz/430 g) Borlotti
    beans, drained and rinsed

1 can (15¾ oz/430 g) black-eyed
    beans, broad beans, or red
    kidney beans, drained and
    rinsed
2 tablespoons ketchup
2 tablespoons molasses
1 teaspoon cider vinegar
½ teaspoon mustard
Juice of ½ lime – optional

---

1   Combine the bacon, garlic, onion, sun-dried tomatoes, chilli flakes and stock in a heavy, wide, non-reactive frying pan. Cover and boil for 7–10 minutes. Uncover and simmer briskly until the onions and garlic are tender and the liquid has boiled down to a syrupy glaze.
2   Add all the beans and stir so they are thoroughly mixed with the onion mixture. Combine together the remaining ingredients except the lime juice and then stir this into the beans. Simmer for 15–20 minutes. Pour in the lime juice, if using, 5 minutes before the beans are done.

Variation:

♡ ⋎ ❅ ▯ ANISE 'BAKED' BEANS

Combine canned, drained Borlotti beans with Anise Tomato Sauce (page 134), a dollop or two of Hoi Sin sauce and a squeeze of lemon juice. Simmer until thoroughly hot.

109

♡ ◯ BROAD-BEAN SWEETCORN STEW

Yields 1½ pts/900 ml

⊕ 25 minutes

Sweetcorn and beans complement one another to form a perfect protein. The native Americans of the area of North America now known as Virginia and the Carolinas made a classic sweetcorn-bean dish called Succotash – it has passed into America's melting pot culinary tradition and is now considered to be basic American food along with bagels, tacos, pizza, chop suey, apple pie and chilli. This recipe for succotash is brightened with tomatoes and basil. For a substantial vegetable main dish serve it in bowls garnished with herbed fromage frais.

6 spring onions, trimmed and sliced thin	Salt and freshly ground pepper to taste
3–4 sun-dried tomatoes, diced with scissors – optional	3–4 tablespoons shredded fresh mint or basil
Approx ½ pt/300 ml stock	6 tablespoons canned, chopped Italian tomatoes
10 oz/275 g frozen broad beans (no need to thaw them first)	8 fl oz/225 ml fromage frais mixed with 2–3 tablespoons mixed chopped fresh mint or basil and coriander
10 oz/275 g frozen sweetcorn kernels (no need to thaw them first)	

1 Combine the onions, sun-dried tomatoes and half the stock in a heavy bottomed, non-reactive frying pan. Cover and boil for 5 minutes. Uncover and simmer until the onions and tomatoes are tender (just a few minutes more).

2 Stir in the broad beans and 2–3 fl oz/50–75 ml stock and simmer, uncovered, until the beans are almost tender, about 5–7 minutes.

3 Stir in the corn, seasoning, mint, canned tomatoes and remaining stock. Simmer uncovered, stirring occasionally, until the vegetables are tender and bathed in a thick sauce, about 10 minutes. Serve with a bowl of fromage frais mixed with the mint or basil and coriander. Garnish each bowlful with a dollop of the Creamy Herb Spread (see page 45).

110

FRIED APPLES

Yields 1 pt/570 ml

🕐 20 minutes

Fried Apples are perfect with sausages patties (see page 60), stuffed into a pork loin steak (see page 57) or served as a vegetable side dish)

1 large onion, halved and sliced into thin half-moons	cored and sliced in ¼-inch/ 0.5-cm wedges
4 fl oz/110 ml medium-dry cider	Approx 6 fl oz/175 ml stock
2 fl oz/50 ml Calvados	Salt and freshly ground pepper to taste
4 Granny Smith apples, peeled,	

1   Combine the onions, cider and Calvados in a heavy bottomed non-reactive saucepan. Cover and boil until the onions are limp and beginning to stick, and the liquid has reduced.
2   Stir in the apples, 4 fl oz/110 ml stock, salt and pepper. Cook briskly, stirring occasionally. Let the apples and onions brown, and begin to stick. Pour in a bit more stock as needed, and stir and scrape up the browned bits from the bottom of the pan. When the apples are tender but not mushy, they are done.

 # 'POPCORN' POTATOES

🕐 25–40 minutes

I call these 'popcorn' potatoes because you can eat them like popcorn; just use your fingers to pop them into your mouth as fast as you can. Don't tell me that you can't serve 'fried' potatoes without resorting to fat and a chip pan! These little darlings bake on a non-stick baking tray until they puff up dramatically and turn crunchy on the outside, floury tender on the inside. They taste *better* than any fried potato you have tried. They taste of potatoes – crunchy, floury *potatoes* do you hear me? – not grease! (I'm trying to stay calm, but topics like this tend to over-excite me.) Just *try them*, then you'll see.

| Tiny new potatoes, scrubbed and dried | Salt – optional |

1 Preheat the oven as high as it will go.
2 Halve the potatoes, spread them out in one layer on a non-stick baking tray. Bake them, stirring them up every once in a while, until they are well browned, puffed up and cooked through. This will take 25–40 minutes, depending on your oven and the size of the potatoes. Tip the potatoes on to a serving platter, salt lightly if desired and serve at once. (Pick them up with your fingers and pop into your mouth, just like popcorn.)

♡ ⚲ ⌗ FRAN LAING'S FAST CHIPS
🕐 20–25 minutes

My recipe for oven-baked, no-grease chips has appeared – in one form or another – in most of my Slim Cuisine books. The chips are a great favourite with my readers. I get many letters extolling their virtues: both adults and children gobble them up in large quantities. Fran Laing sent me her speeded-up variation on my basic recipe. She has cut down the baking time considerably by pre-cooking the potato strips in the microwave, then finishing them in the conventional oven. I'm delighted with the results. The potatoes puff up and they are crunchy on the outside, tender and floury on the inside. And – as always with Slim Cuisine Chips – you taste *potatoes*, not grease.

1 large baking potato

1 Preheat the oven to 425°F, 220°C, gas Mark 7.
2 Don't bother to peel the potato. It tastes best (and it contains the most nutrients) when it is unpeeled. Cut the potato lengthways into strips about 2-inches/5-cm long and 1-inch/2.5-cm thick.
3 Place the chips in one layer on a microwave tray. Microwave on high for 3–4 minutes.
4 Spread the potatoes on to one or two flat baking trays with non-stick coating. Cook in the oven for 7–10 minutes. Loosen the chips with a fish slice and turn each one. bake for a further 5–10 minutes, until browned and puffy. Salt lightly if desired and eat at once.

SMOKY NEW POTATOES

Yields 1½ pts/900ml

🕐 20 minutes

Why not have a 'Vegetable Dinner' a few times a week? A vegetable dinner is a collection of quickly cooked, interesting vegetable dishes served with no meat (except perhaps for a little bit of bacon used – as here – for seasoning). The smoky bacon gives a nice touch to these main-dish, braised potatoes, but vegetarians and non-pork eaters can leave it out and the potatoes will taste just fine. For a feast of complementary tastes and textures try these potatoes, Spiced Carrots (see page 104), Courgettes with Tomatoes (see page 103) and Cucumber–Cherry Tomato Salsa (see page 131).

½ pt/300 ml stock	1 onion, coarsley chopped
1 lb/450 g tiny new potatoes	1 clove garlic, minced
2 slices lean smoked back bacon,	Freshly ground pepper to taste
trimmed and diced	Chopped fresh parsley

---

1   Combine all the ingredients except the parsley in a heavy bottomed frying pan. Cover and boil for 7–10 minutes.
2   Uncover and simmer briskly, stirring occasionally, until the potatoes and onions are 'frying' in the syrupy juices. When the potatoes and onions are tender, remove from the heat and stir in the parsley. Serve at once.

♡ Omit bacon.

Variation:

SMOKY WARM POTATO SALAD

While the potatoes are still warm, stir in about a tablespoon of Balsamic vinegar.

NEW POTATOES WITH COURGETTES

Yields 3 pts/1.7 l

🕐 25 minutes

Courgettes and new potatoes are glorious together; cooked in the microwave they taste almost as if they've been recently plucked from the garden, even if you actually just plucked them from the local Co-op on the way home from work.

1½ lb/700 g new potatoes	Salt and freshly ground pepper to
4 medium courgettes, washed and	taste
trimmed (do not peel)	1 rounded tablespoon grated
4 tablespoons stock	Parmesan cheese
2 tablespoons fresh lemon juice	

---

1 Scrub the potatoes and halve them. Cut the courgettes into ½-inch/1-cm slices.
2 Spread the potatoes out in a 10-inch/25.5-cm square, 2-inch/5-cm deep, microwave-safe, baking dish. Sprinkle on the stock and lemon juice. Cover with cling film. Microwave on high for 5 minutes. Carefully uncover and stir. Re-cover and microwave on high for an additional 5 minutes.
3 Uncover and stir in the courgettes. Cover and microwave on high for 5 minutes. Uncover, season with salt and pepper. Sprinkle evenly with the grated cheese. Cover and allow to stand for 5 minutes.

♡ Omit Parmesan cheese.

 # NEW POTATOES WITH BALSAMIC VINEGAR

Yields 1 pt/570 ml

🕐 20 minutes

New potatoes, halved and microwave-braised with Balsamic vinegar, take on a gorgeous, buttery quality: simple, so quick, and yet so compelling.

---

1 lb/450 g new potatoes, halved	Salt and freshly ground pepper to
4 tablespoons stock	taste
1 scant tablespoon Balsamic vinegar	

Spread the potatoes out in a 10-inch/25.5-cm square, 2-inch/5-cm deep, microwave-safe, baking dish. Sprinkle with the stock and the Balsamic vinegar. Cover tightly and microwave on high for 5 minutes. Uncover, stir, re-cover tightly and microwave on high for another 5 minutes. Uncover and stir once more, re-cover and microwave on high for a final 3 minutes. Uncover, season lightly with salt and pepper and allow to stand for 5 minutes, stirring occasionally. (The potatoes will absorb most of the pan liquid as they stand.)

Variation:

 ## BALSAMIC BRAISED NEW POTATOES WITH BEETROOT–DILL SAUCE

Balsamic Potatoes on a bed of scarlet beetroot sauce make a visually stunning and divine-tasting first course, salad course, or summer-time lunch
New Potatoes with Balsamic vinegar (see page 114)
Beetroot-Dill Sauce (see page 135)
To serve: for each serving spread some of the cold beetroot sauce on to a plate. Arrange a heap of warm Balsamic potato halves on the sauce. Garnish with a sprig of dill.

 ## NEW POTATOES WITH MUSHROOMS

Yields 1½ pts/900 ml

 25 minutes

Potatoes, as a food plant, have been around for thousands of years but still, when the new season rolls around and the tiny new potatoes start to appear in the market, I welcome them as if for the very first time. The little nuggets are so delicious, so compelling, so much fun to cook and eat (and they cook so *fast*) that it pays to indulge every day during their brief season. I love what the microwave does to new potatoes. It seems to preserve their earthy immediacy and it cooks them so they seem about to burst out of their flimsy skins. Try them in the microwave combined with two other earthy favourites, mushrooms and garlic.

4 tablespoons well-seasoned stock	8 oz/225 g firm, closed button
1–2 cloves garlic, crushed	mushrooms, quartered
1 tablespoon chopped parsley	Salt and freshly ground pepper to
1 lb/450 g new potatoes, halved	taste.

Combine all the ingredients except the salt and pepper in a 10-inch/25.5-cm square, 2-inch/5-cm deep, microwave-safe baking dish. Cover tightly and cook for 5 minutes. Uncover, stir, re-cover and cook for another 5 minutes. Once again, uncover, stir, re-cover and cook for a final 5 minutes. Season to taste, stir and let stand uncovered for 5 minutes.

⚟✳MASHED POTATOES WITH SWEDES

Yields 2 pts/1.1 l

🕐 30 minutes

The frozen swedes cook quickly in the microwave, and the potatoes – mixed with boiling, well-seasoned stock – are ready in no time at all. Whip the swedes in the processor, and add a bit of Parmesan cheese and buttermilk or fromage frais, introduce the swedes to the potatoes and dive in.

1 lb/450 g frozen swedes (do not thaw them)	Salt and freshly ground pepper to taste
4 tablespoons stock	Pinch or two cayenne pepper –
16 fl oz/425 ml well-seasoned stock	optional (use if you like things
4 fl oz/110 ml buttermilk or 2-3 tablespoons fromage frais	piquant)
	1 large sachet (4½ oz/120 g)
4 tablespoons grated Parmesan cheese	instant mashed potatoes (see box opposite)

1   Spread the frozen swede out in a 10-inch/25.5-cm square, 2-inch/5-cm deep, microwave-safe baking dish. Sprinkle on 4 tablespoons of the stock. Cover with cling film and microwave on high for 20 minutes, uncovering to stir, and re-covering at 5 minute intervals. Uncover and let stand for 5 minutes.
2   While they are cooking, bring the 16 fl oz/425 ml well-seasoned stock to the boil.
3   Tip the swedes and their juices into the bowl of a blender. Process with the buttermilk or fromage frais until smooth. Sprinkle in the cheese and season to taste with the salt and pepper. Pulse several times to combine.
4   Remove the boiling stock from the heat. Stir the cayenne pepper and instant potatoes into the hot stock. Add the swede mixture. Taste for seasoning. Serve at once.

♡ Omit Parmesan cheese.

Instant Gratification

Alright! So I like packet potatoes – so *sue* me. Don't let a prejudice against packet foods keep you from wallowing in some of the quickest, most delicious potato mixtures ever concocted. Remember, the processing of potatoes is an ancient art. The Incas in the Andes were freeze-drying potatoes thousands of years ago and storing them as dry flakes. Indeed they still do it, but now they've taken it even further – you can buy canned freeze-dried potatoes in South and Central America. If it was good enough for the pre-Columbian Americans (after all, the potato, the tomato, the *cocoa bean* originated with them), then it is certainly good enough for us. The packet potatoes to buy are the kind that come in flakes rather than pellets, and have no fat added to them (read the label). At the time of writing, Mr Mash and Waitrose brand (both made in France) are very good. I see no reason to sully a mashed-potato dinner with chops, roasts or other meaty intrusions. Some really grotty days demand a soothing evening meal of a huge bowl of mash with perhaps some tomato sauce and sautéed mushrooms to make it perfect. Follow the directions on the packet (ignoring, of course, any directions about butter, cream, and milk), but substitute well-seasoned stock for the water. Then stir in a splash or two of buttermilk or a tablespoon or so of fromage frais, sprinkle in a modest shower of grated Parmesan cheese, and sit down in your most comfortable chair with your teddy bear and a *large* spoon.

❄ MASHED POTATO – POLENTA GRATIN

Yields 2½ pts/1.4 l

🕐 15 minutes

Polenta is coarse maize meal used to make a kind of porridge that is one of the starchy wonders of the world. It's often served in a fluffy, golden, well-seasoned heap, to be used much as mashed potatoes are: as a perfect foil for sauces, sautéed mushrooms, caramelized onions and other such delights. Quick-cooking polenta is available in Italian Delis or by mail order (see Mail Order Guide, page 191). I found that instant mashed potato flakes cooked together with quick-cooking polenta in well-seasoned stock – made creamy with buttermilk and flavoured with a bit of grated Parmesan – produce a gratin that carbohy-drate lovers could kill for. It's pretty good as a topping for a Shepherd's Pie, too (see page 48).

32 fl oz/1050 ml well-seasoned stock	6 tablespoons grated Parmesan cheese
4½ oz/135 g quick-cooking polenta	1–2 tablespoons skimmed milk
4½ oz/135 g instant mashed potato flakes	Salt and freshly ground pepper to taste
1 carton (9½ fl oz/284 ml) buttermilk	

1 Preheat the grill.
2 Meanwhile, bring the stock to just below the boil in a heavy bottomed pot. With a wire whisk, stir the polenta and the potato flakes into the liquid. Cook, stirring, for 5–10 minutes until the mixture is very smooth and thick, and has pulled away from the sides of the pan. As the mixture thickens, switch from the whisk to a wooden spoon
3 Remove the pot from the heat. Stir in the buttermilk and 5 tablespoons of the Parmesan cheese. Taste and adjust the seasonings to your taste.
4 Spread the potato-polenta mixture into a 10-inch/25.5-cm deep, glass pie-dish.
5 Sprinkle the milk and remaining cheese over the top. Grill not too close to the heat, for 3–4 minutes, until browned.

Note: The recipe can be prepared ahead of time through to step 3. At serving time, reheat in the microwave on high power for 6 minutes, then sprinkle on the milk and cheese and grill until browned.

♡ Omit Parmesan cheese.

  COLCANNON

Yields 2 pts/1.1 l

🕐 25 minutes

Oh, the terrific things you can do with a packet of mash and some frozen vegetables. Instant gratification and good nutrition, too. Colcannon is a classic mixture of cabbage, spring onions, mashed potatoes, buttermilk . . . and butter. Well – 4 out of 5 isn't bad – in fact it's out of this world.

1 lb/450 g frozen cabbage (do not thaw)

12 (6 oz/175 g) spring onions, trimmed and sliced thin

Juice and grated rind of 1 lemon

1 pt/570 ml well-seasoned stock

Pinch cayenne pepper

1 large packet (4½ oz/135 g) instant potatoes

2–3 tablespoons buttermilk or 1–2 tablespoons fromage frais

Salt and freshly ground pepper to taste

1   Spread the frozen cabbage and the spring onions in a 10-inch/ 25.5-cm square, 2-inch/5-cm deep, microwave-safe baking dish. Sprinkle on the lemon juice and rind, and 4 fl oz/110 ml stock. Cover with microwave cling film and microwave on high for 15 minutes, uncovering to stir and re-covering at 5-minute intervals. Uncover and let stand for 5 minutes.

2   While the cabbage is cooking, bring 16 fl oz/425 ml well-seasoned stock to the boil. Remove from the heat.

3   Stir the cayenne pepper and instant potatoes into the hot stock. Add the buttermilk or fromage frais. Fold in the cabbage mixture. Taste for seasoning. Serve at once.

♡ *Variation*: Try a sort of Mediterranean version of Colcannon by mixing Tomato-Pepper Conserve (see page 102) into the mashed potatoes and buttermilk or fromage frais.

Salads

Salads seem to be classified as either rabbit food (a dieter's nightmare of limp, undressed greens, a few bean sprouts, maybe a wilting carrot slice or two and a flabby radish) or – equally nightmarish for the poor dieter, this time for the opposite reason – olive oil or mayonnaise-drenched, crouton-sprinkled extravaganzas of fat Calories. Why do they have to be either one? I'm giving you a collectoin of very special salad recipes that deliver the taste satisfaction of one type of salad (the fattening type), yet are actually wonders of low-fat and high nutrition.

 ## COUSCOUS SALAD

Yields 2½ pts/1.4 l

⏱ 20 minutes

Couscous is made up of tiny grains of semolina. When the grains are briefly soaked in boiling liquid, they expand and tenderize. Serve couscous (as you would serve rice) hot as an accompaniment to stews and other saucy dishes, or serve it cold, mixed with chopped vegetables and herbs, and dressed with lemon or lime juice, and Balsamic or sherry vinegar. This version of couscous salad bursts with texture and colour. It could easily be the star turn at a summer-time buffet or alfresco feast.

8 fl oz/225 ml boiling, well-seasoned vegetable stock	sliced thin
	1 small courgette, trimmed and diced
6 oz/175 g couscous	
1 can (15¾ oz/440 g) chick peas, well drained	1 small carrot, peeled and diced
	3–4 tablespoons chopped parsley
1 small can (6½ oz/185 g) red peppers, diced	3–4 tablespoons shredded mint
	Freshly ground pepper to taste
3–4 spring onions, trimmed and	Dressing (see below)

1   Combine the boiling stock and couscous in a large bowl. Cover with cling film and let stand for 10 minutes. Uncover and fluff with a fork.
2   Toss in all the remaining ingredients except the dressing.
3   Pour the dressing over the couscous and toss with two spoons. Taste and add more seasonings, Balsamic vinegar and lime juice if necessary.

 Dressing

🕐 15 minutes (prepare this while the couscous is soaking)

½ pint/300 ml vegetable stock	2 cloves garlic, crushed
1½–2½ tablespoons Balsamic vinegar	½ teaspoon ground cumin
	Pinch or two cayenne pepper
1–2 limes	

1   In a small frying pan, combine half the stock, ½ tablespoon Balsamic vinegar, the juice of ½ lime, the garlic, cumin and cayenne pepper. Cover and boil for 5 minutes. Uncover and simmer briskly until the garlic is very tender and the liquid has cooked down to a syrupy glaze.
2   Add the remaining stock and boil until reduced by about half. Stir in an additional tablespoon Balsamic vinegar and the juice of another ½ lime.

⌽ ⊠ POTATO SALAD WITH CHUTNEY

Yields ¾ pt/400 ml

🕑 25 minutes

This potato salad is meant to be eaten warm. New potatoes are cooked – in the microwave – with stock, lemon juice and garlic, and then combined with fromage frais and apple-mango chutney. The salad would be lovely with Quick Poached Chicken Breasts (see page 69) or sliced turkey breast from the Deli counter.

1 lb/450 g tiny new potatoes, halved	1½ tablespoons fromage frais
1 tablespoon stock	Salt and freshly ground pepper to taste
1½ tablespoons lemon juice	3 tablespoons shredded fresh mint
1 clove garlic, crushed	Garnish: shredded fresh mint, chopped parsley and halved cherry tomatoes
1½ tablespoons apple-mango chutney	

1   Combine the potatoes, stock, ½ tablespoon lemon juice and garlic in a 10-inch/25.5-cm square, 2-inch/5.5-cm deep, microwave-safe baking dish. Spread them out in one layer. Cover with microwave cling film and microwave on high for 5 minutes. Uncover, stir, re-cover and microwave for 5 minutes more. Uncover, stir, re-cover and microwave for a final 3 minutes. Let stand for 5 minutes.

2   Spoon the potatoes and their juices into a bowl. Pour the remaining lemon juice over them and stir. Allow to cool slightly. Fold in the chutney and fromage frais and the fresh, shredded mint. Garnish with more mint, shredded parsley and cherry tomatoes.

BLACK-EYED BEAN SALAD
(Texas Caviare)

Yields ½ pt/300 ml

🕑 20 minutes

Black-eyed beans are very popular in the American South. In Texas they eat them marinated (they're referred to affectionately as Texas Caviare); in other parts of the South they serve Hoppin' John – greens, black-eyed beans and ham hocks – every New Year's Day for good luck.

5–6 spring onions, trimmed and sliced thin	1 can (14 oz/400 g) black-eyed beans, drained
4 sun-dried tomatoes, diced (use scissors) – optional	2 tablespoons Balsamic vinegar
1 clove garlic, crushed	1 tablespoon capers, chopped
Grated zest of ½ lime	1 tablespoon fresh parsley, chopped
Juice of 1 lime	1 tablespoon fresh coriander, chopped – optional
½ pt/300 ml stock	

1   Combine the onions, sun-dried tomatoes, garlic, lime zest, juice of ½ lime and stock in a heavy bottomed frying pan. Cover and boil for 7–10 minutes. Uncover and simmer briskly, stirring occasionally, until the onion is tender and the juices have cooked down to a syrupy glaze.

2   Toss in the remaining ingredients. Refrigerate until needed.

 ## SWEET-AND-SOUR ARTICHOKES

Yields 1½ pts/900 ml

 15 minutes

Artichoke hearts in brine are a store-cupboard treasure. Mixed with sultanas that have been plumped in vermouth, dressed with Balsamic vinegar and lemon juice, they make an almost instant relish, salad or snack. Sweet-and-Sour Artichokes are delicious eaten cold right out of the fridge, and they will keep for a week, so it pays to make a whole batch. But if you feel that it is too much, the recipe can easily be halved.

6 oz/175 g sultanas	Juice of 1 large lemon
8 fl oz/225 ml dry white vermouth	2 tablespoons Balsamic vinegar or sherry vinegar
2 cans (14 oz/400 g each) artichoke hearts in brine, drained and quartered	Freshly ground pepper

1   Simmer the sultanas and vermouth in a frying pan until the liquid is absorbed and the sultanas are plump.

2   Toss in a bowl with the remaining ingredients.

3   Serve at room temperature.

SWEET-AND-SOUR PEPPERS

Yields 1 pt/570 ml

⏲ 20 minutes

If you are in the habit of peeling peppers before you use them you will find that the peeling is really very quick and easy – about as easy as peeling carrots or potatoes. By now you know how I feel about peeling peppers: the peeling vastly improves the texture, taste and digestibility of the finished dish. Simply stem and seed the peppers, cut them into their natural sections and peel each section with a swivel-bladed peeler. If time is really short, you might try cooking the liquids down to a thick syrup and then tossing in an equivalent amount of canned or jarred red peppers, cut into strips. Yes, it will be a compromise, but still – not too bad considering the little time it takes. Sweet-and-sour red peppers can be served as a relish or a vegetable side dish. The vivid colour and deep taste will brighten any meal.

Approx 3 red peppers, peeled, seeded and cut into strips	*2 fl oz/50 ml sherry*
Approx 3 yellow peppers, peeled, seeded and cut into strips	*Dash or two of each: Balsamic vinegar and Teriyaki sauce*
8 fl oz/225 ml stock	*Few drops fresh lemon juice*
	Freshly ground pepper to taste

1   Combine all the ingredients in a heavy bottomed pot. Cook over a moderately high heat, stirring occasionally, until the peppers are tender and the juices are scant, thick and syrupy. Add more stock during the cooking as needed. Taste and add salt, more pepper or more lemon juice to your taste. Serve warm or well chilled.

 BEETROOT IN ORANGE CREAM

Yields 1¼ pts/700 ml

⏲ 10 minutes

The 'cream' refers to buttermilk which has the consistency of pouring cream and the flavour of sour cream. If you can't find buttermilk, substitute fromage frais that has been thinned with a little skimmed milk. Vacuum-packed beetroot in natural juices are readily available in the fresh vegetable section of many supermarkets. Beware those packed with vinegar. The acrid vinegar totally masks the distinctive sweet-earthy taste of the beetroot.

4–6 ready cooked, peeled beetroot (the kind that contains no vinegar)	6 fl oz/175 ml buttermilk
	1 tablespoon Balsamic vinegar
	1 teaspoon crumbled dried tarragon
1 tablespoon French Mustard	Freshly ground pepper
1 tablespoon orange juice concentrate	

1   Slice the beetroot ¼-inch/0.5-cm thick. Put the slices into a bowl with their juices.
2   Stir in the mustard and orange juice concentrate into a small bowl. Slowly whisk in the buttermilk, then the vinegar. Sprinkle in the tarragon and pepper and stir to combine.
3   Pour the dressing over the beetroot and gently fold together. Refrigerate until needed.

CHERRY TOMATO, MANGO AND BASIL SALAD

Yields 1 pt/570 ml

⏱ 10 minutes

Cherry tomatoes are available all the year round, and they always taste like *tomatoes*, which is more than I can say about lots of other varieties of supermarket tomatoes. Halved, combined with cubes of ripe mango and shredded fresh basil and served with a mayonnaise–textured mango dressing on the side, it will knock the socks off the most blasé diners.

24 cherry tomatoes (if yellow ones are in season, use 6 yellow, 18 red)	3 tablespoons shredded basil leaves (if basil is unavailable, substitute mint)
1 ripe mango, peeled and diced (see box, page 127)	Mango Mayonnaise (see below)

1   Halve the cherry tomatoes and put them in a bowl. Gently mix the mango with the tomatoes. Sprinkle on the basil.
2   Put the Mango 'Mayonnaise' in a pretty bowl and set it in the centre of an attractive platter. Surround the bowl with the tomato-mango mixture. Let the diners help themselves to salad and dressing.

To Peel and Cube a Mango

1   Cube the mango as follows: with a sharp knife slice the mango as if you were slicing it in half, but try to miss the large flat stone. Slice down again on the other side of the stone. You will now have two half mangoes and the flat centre to which clings quite a bit of mango flesh. With a small, sharp paring knife score each mango half lengthwise and crosswise, cutting all the way to, but not through, the skin. Push out the skin as if you were pushing the half mango inside out. The mango flesh will stand out in cubes. Slice these cubes off the skin.

2   Peel the skin from the centre slice. Either slice the mango flesh off the stone and use the trimmings for the mango mayonnaise (see below), or tie a tea-towel around your neck, lean over the kitchen sink and gnaw the juicy mango flesh off the stone. It's messy, succulent and utterly delicious – it's the cook's reward!

MANGO 'MAYONNAISE'

Yields ½ pt/300 ml

⏲ 5 minutes

Yes, yes, yes, I know that this is not mayonnaise, of course it isn't – how could it be? Mayonnaise is pure fat – an emulsion of egg yolks and oil. Mayonnaise is – some say – an exquisite sauce. Indeed, I myself used to believe it. But ten years ago, when I managed – through sheer determination and will power – to lose almost six stones, my life changed. In order to *keep* the weight off, and to improve my health, I gave up added fat and began developing the cooking techniques that have become Slim Cuisine. Ten years of eating food that has *not* been adulterated with fat has changed my taste perceptions; my palate can no longer tolerate the taste and texture of fats and oils. To me, mayonnaise – no matter how virgin the olive oil or how impeccable the technique – is no longer exquisite. But this Mango Dressing: now *that* is what I call exquisite!

1 *whole, ripe mango, peeled and diced (see above)*	1 *tablespoon buttermilk*
2 *tablespoons fromage frais*	*Dash Worcestershire sauce*
2 *tablespoons Balsamic vinegar or sherry vinegar*	*Pinch dry mustard*
	Pinch or two brown sugar, to taste

1   Put all the mango flesh into a blender.
2   Whisk together the remaining ingredients except the sugar.
     Add this sauce to the mango. Process until perfectly smooth.
     Taste and add a pinch or two of brown sugar if necessary.
     Refrigerate until needed.

 CUCUMBER SALAD

Yields 1 pt/570 ml

10 minutes

Peel a cucumber, cut it in half lengthwise and scoop out the seeds
with a teaspoon, then slice the halves into thin half moons: it
takes minimal time, and gives you the main ingredient for a
number of interesting salads. For this one, the cucumber slices are
bathed in a buttermilk–mustard sauce.

1 carton (9½ fl oz/284 ml) buttermilk (or use fromage frais that has been thinned with a little skimmed milk)	Salt and freshly ground pepper to taste
2 teaspoons Dijon mustard	1 large cucumber, peeled, halved, seeded and sliced into ¼-inch/ 0.5-cm slices
1 tablespoon Balsamic vinegar	

1   Whisk together the buttermilk, mustard, vinegar, salt and
     pepper.
2   Fold the cucumber into this dressing. Chill until needed.

 DILLED CUCUMBER SALAD

Yields 1 pt/570 ml

10 minutes

This version of cucumber salad has a Hungarian origin. I find that
the flavour of the cultured buttermilk, available in many supermarkets, has something in common with the flavour of the
soured cream used in so many Hungarian recipes.

1 carton (9½ fl oz/284 ml) buttermilk (or use fromage frais that has been thinned with a little skimmed milk)	3 tablespoons snipped fresh dill
	1 large cucumber, peeled, halved, seeded and sliced into ¼-inch/ 0.5-cm thick slices
1 tablespoon cider vinegar	Salt and freshly ground pepper to
1 teaspoon granulated NutraSweet	taste

Lavish and colourful vegetarian fare in the conservatory: a
vibrant piperade (tomato-pepper conserve) flan, surrounded by
(clockwise from lower right): mushroom pâté; sweet and sour
artichokes; garlic-sun-dried tomato bread; broad bean-sweetcorn
stew with herbed fromage frais; creamy stuffed pears.

An exciting lunch brightens the busiest day: clockwise from upper left: chive-mustard seed bread with curried apricot spread; smoked turkey sandwiches; spicy corn soup; strawberry jam-filled angel buns; pork-apple sausage patties and 'fried' apples in pitta bread.

1 Whisk together the buttermilk, vinegar, NutraSweet and dill.
2 Fold the cucumber into this dressing and season with salt and pepper. Chill until needed.

 COLE SLAW

Yields 3 pts/1.7 l

⏱ 25 minutes

Cole Slaw (shredded cabbage salad) comes in many guises. This version is based on the 'health salad' served at New York's 2nd Avenue Deli. The 2nd Avenue Deli is one of the last remaining bastions of New York Jewish Deli food – the real thing. This adaptation is *not* the real thing: I have substituted Balsamic vinegar for the oil and white vinegar, and NutraSweet for the sugar. Interestingly enough, while this recipe was in progress, my staff and I had a blind tasting of several versions of the cole slaw, and the one with the NutraSweet was unanimously rated the best – the texture and taste was better than the sugar version.

12 oz/350 g cabbage, shredded in a food processor (use the slicing disc	*Salt*
	2 fl oz/50 ml cider vinegar
	2 fl oz/50 ml Balsamic vinegar
10 oz/275 g peppers, peeled and thinly sliced (use the slicing disc)	*1 tablespoon granulated Nutrasweet*
	Freshly ground pepper to taste
12 oz/350 g carrots, peeled, and grated in a food processor (use the grating disc)	

1 Combine the cabbage, peppers and carrots in a non-reactive colander. Sprinkle on some salt (no need to be lavish – a sprinkling will do) and toss with two spoons. Allow to sit for 10 minutes.
2 With your hands, squeeze out any excess moisture. Combine the vegetables in a bowl with the remaining ingredients.
3 Place in a covered storage container, leave in a refrigerator until needed and shake occasionally to mix.

♡ ⓥⓒ STORE-CUPBOARD CORN SALAD

Yields 1½ pts/900 ml

🕐 5 minutes

Corn Salad is the sort of dish I like to make in quantity, and then snack on, whenever I have the need (it happens *often*) for something delicious to eat while standing up in front of the refrigerator. The salad also makes a beautiful addition to a buffet table – or to an ordinary, everyday meal for that matter.

---

2 cans (7 oz/200 g each) sweetcorn, drained
6 canned tomatoes, drained and coarsely chopped
6 canned red peppers (pimientos), drained and coarsely chopped
½ small can (4 oz/110 g) mild green chillies, drained and coarsely chopped

Salt and freshly ground pepper to taste
2 fl oz/50 ml Balsamic vinegar
1 tablespoon castor sugar
2 tablespoons each: chopped fresh coriander – optional, chopped fresh parsley, snipped chives.

---

1   Combine all the ingredients in a shallow dish. Toss together until the sugar is dissolved.
2   Refrigerate until needed.

STORE-CUPBOARD TOMATO-PEPPER SALSA

Yields 3 pts/1.7 l

🕐 5 minutes

Salsa means – simply – sauce, but a salsa is really a sort of hybrid combination of sauce, salad and relish. This salsa is based on the table salsas served in Mexico, and in the South-West of the United States. Use it as a salad relish for Mexican food (Fajitas, page 51 for instance, or Mexican Shepherd's Pie, page 48) or serve it as a dip with raw vegetable dippers, toasted pitta-bread triangles, or fat-free savoury biscuits, such as matzo crackers or Hi-Lo biscuits.

---

2 cans (1 lb 12 oz/800 g each) Italian tomatoes, well drained
1 can (approx 14 oz/400 g) red peppers, well drained
Canned chillies, well drained and chopped (to taste)

2 fl oz/50 ml red-wine vinegar
2 cloves garlic, minced
2 tablespoons chopped fresh parsley
2 tablespoons chopped fresh mint

---

1   Chop the tomatoes and peppers with kitchen scissors. Combine all the ingredients in a non-reactive bowl. Chill thoroughly.

CUCUMBER–CHERRY TOMATO SALSA

Yields 2 pts/1.1 l

⊕ 15 minutes

This salsa is a crunchy, bracing relish of cucumbers, cherry tomatoes, capers, chilli, garlic and herbs. If yellow cherry tomatoes are in season, use a combo of half-red, half-yellow for a visually stunning dish.

---

2 boxes (9 oz/250 g each) cherry tomatoes, stemmed and quartered
1 long cucumber, peeled, halved, seeded and sliced thin
1 chilli pepper, minced
1 tablespoon small capers
2 teaspoons caper brine
1½ tablespoons Balsamic vinegar
1–2 cloves garlic, crushed (the amount depends on your taste, if you hate garlic, leave it out)

Juice of ½ lime
3 spring onions, trimmed and sliced thin
2 tablespoons chopped fresh parsley
2 tablespoons chopped fresh coriander
2 tablespoons shredded fresh mint
Freshly ground pepper to taste

Combine all the ingredients. Allow to stand at room temperature until serving time. (Stir it occasionally.)

 FRUIT-FENNEL SALSA

Yields ¾ pt/400 ml

⊕ 10 minutes

Another relish-like salsa, this time with the interesting combination of mango, orange, fennel and chilli. They all work together brilliantly. The salsa is a splendid complement to Steamed White Fish Fillets (see page 77), Quick Poached Chicken Breasts (see page 69) or Roasted Honey-Mustard Tenderloin (see page 55). For a spectacular first course, serve slices of smoked salmon or fillets of smoked trout garnished with fruit-fennel salsa.

1 orange, peeled and diced
1 mango, peeled and diced (see box, page 127)
1 head fennel, trimmed and diced
½ small chilli, minced, or to taste – optional

1 tablespoon chopped fresh mint
1 tablespoon chopped fresh parsley
4 tablespoons fresh orange juice
2 tablespoons fresh lime juice
Salt and freshly ground pepper to taste

Combine ingredients, and refrigerate until needed.

Sauces

Two categories of ingredients are important to low-fat sauce making: skimmed milk dairy products and cooked vegetables. If you enrich skimmed milk with skimmed milk powder, your white sauces will never have the watery, insipid quality that can mar so many no-fat white sauces. And buttermilk with its creaminess and delicious soured-cream flavour, combined with quark or fromage frais, can be used for all sorts of interesting cold sauces.

Puréed cooked vegetables – beetroot for instance, or peppers, or pulses – can be used to make the base for some very satisfying sauces. Canned beans, canned or jarred peppers (pimientos) and vacuum-packed beetroot in natural juice are terrific; if you keep your kitchen well stocked with these, infinite quick sauces are always possible.

 **INSTANT TOMATO SAUCE**

Yields approx ¾ pt/400 ml

🕐 20 minutes

Tomato sauce is one of the most versatile home-cooked sauces. Use it on pasta, as a sauce for lean meats and fish, with mashed potatoes – one of my readers insists that she loves it spread on her morning toast! With excellent canned Italian tomatoes available in virtually every supermarket, home-made tomato sauce is simple to make. It was my twenty-year-old son, however, who showed me how to make *instant* tomato sauce. His London kitchen is so small that – were I still 15½ stones as I was in the old days – I wouldn't be able to cram myself in. You don't *stand* in Shawm's kitchen, you *wear* it. He prepares delicious tomato sauce on his Baby Belling by opening a box of tomato passata, emptying it into a pan, applying plenty of freshly ground pepper, herbs and so on, and then uses it to blanket Cappeletti, little pizzas built on bagels, or spaghetti. I've taken his idea and refined it a little: make an infusion first of spring onions, diced sun-dried tomatoes (if you have them), garlic and seasonings, then stir in the passata and simmer for 10 minutes. The whole thing takes only about 15 minutes, and the sauce is marvellous. Obviously, all sorts of variations can be played on the basic theme.

5–6 spring onions, trimmed and sliced	Pinch or two dried red chilli flakes
	Pinch or two dried oregano
3–4 sun-dried tomatoes, chopped (use scissors)	6–8 fl oz/175–225 ml stock
	1 box (1 lb 2 oz/500 g) passata
1–2 cloves of garlic, minced	Freshly ground pepper to taste

1   Combine the onions, sun-dried tomatoes, garlic, chilli, oregano and stock in a non-reactive frying pan. Cover and boil for 3–4 minutes. Uncover and simmer until the onions and garlic are tender and the liquid has cooked down considerably and become syrupy.

2   Stir in the passata and grind in some pepper. Simmer for approximately 10 minutes.

Variation:

🧸♡🥕❄🯁 ANISE TOMATO SAUCE

Yields approx ¾ pt/400 ml

🕐 20 minutes

4–5 spring onions, trimmed and sliced	½ teaspoon anise or fennel seeds
3–4 sun-dried tomatoes, chopped (use scissors)	6–8 fl oz/175–225 ml stock
	1 box (1 lb 2 oz/500 g) passata
1–2 cloves garlic, crushed	Freshly ground pepper to taste
1 thin slice ginger, peeled and crushed	
Pinch or two dried red chilli flakes	

134

1　Combine the onions, sun-dried tomatoes, garlic, chilli, anise seeds and stock in a non-reactive frying pan. Cover and boil for 3–4 minutes. Uncover and simmer until the onions and garlic are tender.
2　Stir in the passata and grind in some pepper. Simmer for 10–15 minutes.

 ## BEETROOT-DILL SAUCE

Yields ¾ pt/400 ml

 5 minutes

Beetroot, puréed in the processor, makes a flamboyantly scarlet purée. If you flavour the purée with lemon, dill and chives you have a beautiful sauce for cold potatoes, or vegetables, or a dip for raw vegetables or toasted pitta-bread triangles. It's pretty good spooned right out of its bowl, too.

1 pack (9 oz/250 g) beetroot in natural juice	5 tablespoons snipped fresh dill
4 fl oz/110 ml buttermilk or fromage frais	3–4 tablespoons snipped chives
Juice and rind of ½ lemon	Salt and freshly ground pepper to taste

1　Cut the beetroot into chunks. Combine them and their liquid in the container of a food processor with the remaining ingredients.
2　Blend to a rough purée. Taste and adjust seasonings.

Variation:

 ## BEETROOT SAUCE WITH GARLIC

Substitute orange juice and rind for the lemon. Crush a clove of garlic and marinate it in the juice for 5–10 minutes. Omit the dill. Process all the ingredients to a rough purée

WHITE SAUCE

Yields 1 pt/570 ml

10 minutes

In the gastronomic world, white sauce comes in and out of fashion. During the height of the Nouvelle Cuisine movement, white sauces were considered hopelessly un-chic, even unhealthy. It wasn't the fat level that was considered unhealthy, it was the flour. Since many Nouvelle Cuisine sauces involved boiling down pints of cream to a mere puddle, it was obvious that butterfat was never considered a problem, but I never could understand the health objection to a little bit of flour. A classic white sauce begins with a butter/flour roux into which full-fat milk or half-cream is incorporated. It's an infinitely useful sauce, and a little flour never hurt anyone. But oh! the butterfat! You might as well butter your arteries and have done with it.

I've developed a white sauce that can be prepared in the microwave in about 5 minutes. The cooking vessel is an ordinary 3½ pt/2 litre opaque white plastic measuring jug (see box, page 189). The sauce is made with skimmed milk (I use the longlife cartons – they are always on hand) and cornflour – it *sounds* awful, I know. But keep this in mind: skimmed milk powder is stirred into the skimmed milk to give it a lovely richness and when the sauce is used in various recipes (see Cauliflower Cheese, page 96 and Aubergine Gratin, page 97 as examples) flavourful infusions are added to the basic sauce to give it depth and pizzazz. As a result, the sauce is very good and – of course – incredibly versatile. When used in gratins and other recipes, it tastes so *fattening*, yet it is virtually fat-free. The texture of the sauce should be creamy but not pasty. You will soon learn the exact timing to produce a perfectly textured sauce in your own particular microwave.

---

6 tablespoons skimmed milk powder	Approx 18 fl oz/500 ml skimmed
3 tablespoons cornflour	milk (1 longlife carton)
Salt and freshly ground pepper to taste	

---

1   Measure the milk powder and cornflour into a 3½ pt/2 l, 7-inch/18-cm top diameter, opaque white plastic measuring jug (see box,page 189). Sprinkle on the salt and pepper.
2   With a wire whisk, mix the milk thoroughly into the dry ingredients – you don't want lumps. Vigorous whisking helps alleviate the chance of volcanic eruptions. Cover the jug tightly with cling film.
3   Microwave on full power for 3 minutes. Carefully (avert your face, and begin with the side *away* from you, to release the steam. Be careful – the steam is hot) uncover and whisk thoroughly. Re-cover tightly and microwave for another 2 minutes. Carefully uncover, whisk, re-cover tightly and microwave for a final 1½–2 minutes, until boiled, thickened and smooth.

4   Whisk and allow to stand for 3–4 minutes. Taste and adjust seasonings if necessary. Store in the refrigerator with a sheet of microwave cling film resting directly on the surface of the sauce.

To Reheat: If the sauce has thickened too much overnight in the refrigerator, whisk in some skimmed milk to thin it to the desired consistency. Cover the jug with cling film and microwave with 30 second bursts, stopping to whisk well between each, until the sauce is warm and smooth. It is important to follow these directions because a cornflour-bound sauce – if overheated – may break down.

 # CHEESE SAUCE

Yields 1 pt/570 ml

🕐 10 minutes

Fold a few tablespoons of grated Parmesan cheese into the basic white sauce recipe, and you have a cheese sauce that simply begs for a pot of freshly cooked macaroni or a head of perfectly cooked cauliflower.

6 tablespoons skimmed milk powder	*3–4 tablespoons grated Parmesan*
3 tablespoons cornflour	*cheese*
Approx 18 fl oz/500 ml skimmed	*Salt and freshly ground pepper to*
milk (1 longlife carton)	*taste*

1   Measure the milk powder and cornflour into a 3½ pt/2 l, 7-inch/18-cm top diameter, opaque white plastic measuring jug (see box, page 189).
2   With a wire whisk, mix the milk thoroughly in the dry ingredients – you don't want lumps. Vigorous whisking helps alleviate the chance of volcanic eruptions. Cover the jug tightly with cling film.
3   Microwave on full power for 3 minutes. Carefully uncover (avert your face, and begin with the side *away* from you, to release the steam. Be careful – the steam is hot) and whisk thoroughly. Re-cover tightly and microwave for another 2 minutes. Carefully uncover, whisk, re-cover tightly and microwave for a final 1½–2 minutes, until boiled, thickened and smooth.
4   With a rubber spatula fold the grated Parmesan cheese into the sauce. Season to taste. Let stand for 3–4 minutes. Taste and adjust seasonings if necessary. Store in the refrigerator with a sheet of microwave cling film resting directly over the surface of the sauce.

♡ ⌇⊟⊠ MUSTARDY WHITE SAUCE

Yields approx 1 pt/570 ml

⏰ 10 minutes

When cooked, Dijon mustard loses its bite, so this version of white sauce has a rich mustardy dimension, but is in no way searing. The sauce is splendid with cooked vegetables, button mushrooms, macaroni, or Quick Poached Chicken Breasts (see page 69).

---

6 tablespoons skimmed milk powder
3 tablespoons cornflour
Approx 18 fl oz/500 ml skimmed milk (1 longlife carton)

2 rounded tablespoons Dijon mustard
Salt and freshly ground pepper to taste

---

1   Measure the milk powder and cornflour into a 3½ pt/2 l, 7-inch/18-cm top diameter, opaque plastic measuring jug (see box, page 189).
2   With a wire whisk, mix the milk thoroughly into the dry ingredients. Whisk in the mustard, stirring well – you don't want lumps. Vigorous whisking helps alleviate the chance of volcanic eruptions. Cover the jug tightly with cling film.
3   Microwave on full power for 3 minutes. Carefully uncover (avert your face, and begin with the side *away* from you, to release the steam. Be careful – the steam is hot) and whisk thoroughly. Re-cover tightly and microwave for another 2 minutes. Carefully uncover, whisk, re-cover tightly and microwave for a final 1½–2 minutes, until boiled, thickened and smooth.
4   Whisk and allow to stand for 3–4 minutes. Season to taste. Store in the refrigerator with a sheet of microwave cling film resting directly over the surface of the sauce.

⌇⊠ GARLIC–BLACK PEPPER SAUCE

Yields 1 pt/570 ml

⏰ 10 minutes

When garlic is cooked in an infusion, as it is here, it takes on an irresistible sweet mellowness. The pepper adds bite. If you wish, leave out the pepper for a gentler effect.

4–5 large cloves garlic, peeled and roughly crushed ½ pt/300 ml stock Freshly ground pepper (10–12 twists of the peppermill)	1 recipe White Sauce (see page 135), or Cheese sauce (see page 137), or Mustardy White sauce (see page 138)

1   Combine all the ingredients, except the sauce, in a heavy bottomed frying pan. Cover and boil for 5–7 minutes.
2   Uncover and simmer very briskly until the garlic is meltingly tender and the stock has cooked down to a syrupy glaze.
3   Stir the infusion (use a rubber spatula to get every bit out of the frying pan) into Slim Cuisine White Sauce, Cheese Sauce, or Mustardy White Sauce.

♡   If you are using a sauce that contains Parmesan cheese, leave out the cheese.

♡ ◊ ◻ CANNELLINI–PIMIENTO SAUCE

Yields ¾ pt/400 ml

🕐 10 minutes

This sauce is a variation of the dip on page 44. It is quite good as a pasta sauce, or with steamed fish.

1 can (15¾ oz/430 g) cannellini beans 2 cans (6½ oz/185 g each) red peppers (pimientos) 3 cloves garlic, crushed Good pinch dried chilli flakes ¼ teaspoon ground cumin seed	4–5 sun-dried tomatoes, diced (use scissors) – optional ½ pt/300 ml stock Salt and freshly ground pepper to taste Few drops lemon juice

1   Empty the beans and peppers into a colander. Rinse under cold water and set aside to drain well.
2   Combine the garlic, chillies, cumin, tomatoes and stock in a non-reactive frying pan. Cover and boil for 3–4 minutes. Uncover and simmer until the garlic is tender and the liquid has cooked down considerably and become syrupy.
3   Combine the drained beans and peppers in the food processor container. Season with the salt and pepper. Process to a rough purée.
4   Scrape the purée into the frying pan with the garlic-spice infusion. Add a few drops of lemon juice. Simmer gently for a few minutes to blend the flavours. Taste and adjust seasonings.

Bread

Why is baking bread such a satisfying experience? There is something elemental and almost mystical about it: the baking of cakes and biscuits doesn't even come close to approximating the feeling of profound accomplishment that bread-baking engenders. I'll never forget my first loaf. It was made simply from yeast, flour, salt and water, and baked free-form on a cornmeal-sprinkled baking tray. The bread had a crunchy crust that shattered when you bit into it, leaving ambrosial shards on the tablecloth, and the crumb (as the inside of a loaf is called) was very slightly chewy, not too fine grained and deliciously wheaty: in other words, it was a stunning – let's not beat about the bush – practically perfect loaf of bread. The urge to rush headlong into the street in order to press crusty chunks of this masterpiece on helpless passers-by was very strong. I've baked thousands of beautiful loaves since that first time – indeed for a while I taught bread-baking seminars, and had a great time introducing my students to the exhilaration of home bread-baking.

Old-fashioned yeast bread-baking takes time: setting the sponge, kneading, first risings, second risings and finally the actual baking – it can be hours (for some breads, even a day or two) before the loaf is ready for that first exultant taste. All of my students worked outside their homes and many of them would go to great lengths to manipulate their days so that they could

141

rush home a couple of times during the day to tend the bread dough, and then, in the evening, proudly serve a freshly baked loaf to their families. (Many of these students were men – indeed it seemed to be the *men* who became really obsessed with bread baking.)

Once you get your hands into yeast dough and feel how responsive it is, how it comes to life under your hands, you begin to understand how such obsessions can come about: it really is an addictive activity. But is it practical? On working weekdays getting your hands into yeast dough is not only too time-consuming – it is too distracting. It makes sense to save the full sensuality of proper yeast bread-making – the kneading, the rising, the punching – for weekends and holidays.

During the week, there are shortcuts to daily home-baked bread. For instance, you could bake Irish soda bread. Soda bread, which takes no yeast at all, can be slapped together in minutes out of the simplest ingredients and heaved into an oven on a flat baking sheet. It emerges, hot and crusty, approximately forty minutes later. No yeast to pamper, no risings, and – this is important – very little mess. And basic Irish Soda bread – like many classics – gives wonderful opportunity for variation, both sweet and savoury. Or you might try the three yeast-bread recipes at the end of this chapter. They cut more corners than I would have thought possible. You won't need to manipulate your work day to bake these sensible and practical loaves. Of course, you'll miss some of the fun of kneading, rising, punching, but, when time is of the essence, practicality is all.

 WHEATEN BREAD

Yields 1 loaf

🕒 40–45 minutes

Simple and almost ridiculously easy: simply mix self-raising flours (half-brown, half-white) and buttermilk (or fromage frais thinned with skimmed milk) in a bowl, knead a few times right in the bowl, shape into a free-form loaf and bake on a flat tray. The resulting bread is plain, honest and delicious. The character of soda bread is quite different from that of yeast bread, but in its own way it is *good* bread. Should you have any left on the next day, it makes excellent toast.

8 oz/225 g white self-raising	½–¾ pt/300–400 ml buttermilk
sponge flour	(or 9 fl oz/275 ml fromage frais
8 oz/225 g brown self-raising flour	thinned with 6 fl oz/175 ml
Pinch salt	skimmed milk)

1   Preheat the oven to 400°F, 200°C, Gas Mark 6.
2   Combine the flours and salt in a large bowl. Lightly mix with your hand. Make a well in the middle of the flour.
3   Pour ½ pt/300 ml buttermilk (or thinned fromage frais) into the well. With a wooden spoon, stir the flour into the buttermilk. When the mixture forms a cohesive mass, knead it a few turns, right in the bowl. If the dough is too crumbly, add a bit more buttermilk; if too wet, a bit more flour, but the dough should remain slightly sticky.
4   Form the dough into a plump round loaf and place it on a lightly floured, non-stick baking tray. With a sharp knife, cut a shallow cross on the top. Bake for 35–40 minutes. When done, it will sound hollow when tapped on the bottom and it will be beautifully browned. Cool on a rack.

 ## ❋ WHEATEN BREAD WITH HONEY

Yields 1 loaf

⊕ 40–45 minutes

Adding a little honey to basic wheaten soda bread gives it a hint of sweetness – perfect for breakfast or for tea.

8 oz/225 g white self-raising	½–¾ pt/300–400 ml buttermilk
sponge flour	(or 9 fl oz/275 ml fromage frais
8 oz/225 g brown self-raising	thinned with 6 fl oz/175 ml
flour	skimmed milk)
Pinch salt	2 tablespoons honey

1   Preheat the oven to 400°F, 200°C, Gas Mark 6.
2   Put the flours into a large bowl. Sprinkle the salt over it. Lightly mix with your hand. Make a well in the middle of the flour.
3   Pour ½ pt/300 ml buttermilk (or thinned fromage frais) into the well. With a wooden spoon, stir the flour into the buttermilk. Add the honey and more buttermilk as needed to form a rather rough, slightly sticky dough that gathers together in a mass. If too crumbly and dry, add a bit more buttermilk: if too wet, a bit more flour. Lightly knead it, right

in the bowl, for a few turns. Sprinkle on a bit more flour so that the dough is workable, but it should remain slightly sticky. Don't overwork it.

4   Form the dough into a plump round loaf and place it on a lightly floured, non-stick baking tray. Cut a shallow cross in the top. Bake in the oven for 35–45 minutes. When done, it will sound hollow when tapped on the bottom and it will be beautifully browned. Cool on a rack.

 # FAST PUMPERNICKEL

Yields 1 large loaf

45–50 minutes

Real pumpernickel bread is a dark (almost black) rye. I've added some of the flavour and colour components of pumpernickel to the basic soda-bread formula. The result is – of course – not really a pumpernickel, but it *is* a wonderfully robust-tasting black bread, perfect for sandwiches (sliced turkey breast and mustard, roasted pork tenderloin and chutney, poached chicken breast medallions and puréed beetroot – you get the idea).

1½ oz/40 g low-fat, unsweetened cocoa powder
8 oz/225 g white self-raising flour
8 oz/225 g brown self-raising flour
Pinch salt
1–2 rounded tablespoons caraway seeds

½–¾ pt/300–400 ml buttermilk (or 9 fl oz/275 ml fromage frais thinned with 6 fl oz/175 ml skimmed milk)
3 tablespoons molasses
Sprinkling maize meal (polenta)

---

1   Preheat the oven to 400°F, 200°C, Gas Mark 6.
2   Sift together into a large bowl the cocoa, flours and salt. Sprinkle the caraway seeds over the top. Make a well in the middle of the flour.
3   Pour ½ pt/300 ml buttermilk (or thinned fromage frais) into the well. With a wooden spoon, stir the flour into the buttermilk. Add the molasses and more buttermilk as needed to form a rather rough, slightly sticky dough. Lightly knead for a few turns. The dough should remain sticky and rough. Don't overwork it or the bread will be tough. Add more flour as needed.
4   Form the dough into a plump round loaf and place it on a lightly floured, non-stick baking tray that is sprinkled with

maize meal. Cut a shallow cross in the top. Bake in the oven for 35–45 minutes. When done, it will be crusty and will sound hollow when tapped on the bottom. Cool on a rack.

What's in a Name?

The legend is as follows: a horseman (perhaps even Napoleon) paused for refreshment in a small Eastern European town. He wearily dismounted from his trusty horse, Nicole, and looked around for sustenance. A helpful peasant offered him some coarse black bread. The fastidious horseman took one look at the rustic stuff and turned away. *'Bon pour Nicole* (good for my horse)', he sniffed disdainfully. And (so they say) pumpernickel was given the name that has stuck with it ever since. Of course there is an alternative explanation: the name of the baker who first baked the coarse black loaf was Pumpernickel. Personally, I opt for the romance of the weary soldier and his trusty horse.

CHEESE BREAD

Yields 1 large loaf

 40–45 minutes

Add grated Parmesan cheese to white soda bread dough to make a splendid cheese bread, good for toasting, for sandwiches, or to serve with dinner to mop up delicious sauces.

---

1 lb/450 g white self-raising flour	½–¾ pt/300–400 ml buttermilk
2 pinches salt	(or 9 fl oz/275 ml fromage frais
Freshly ground pepper to taste (be	thinned with 6 fl oz/175 ml
generous)	skimmed milk)
6 tablespoons grated Parmesan	
cheese	

---

1 Preheat the oven to 400°F, 200°C, Gas Mark 6.
2 Put the flour in a large bowl. Sprinkle the salt, pepper and cheese all over it. Lightly mix with your hand. Make a well in the middle of the flour.
3 Pour ½ pt/300 ml buttermilk (or thinned fromage frais) into the well. With a wooden spoon, stir the flour into the

buttermilk. Add more buttermilk or fromage frais, as needed, to form a rather rough, slightly sticky dough that forms into a cohesive mass. Knead the dough lightly for a few turns right in the bowl. The dough should remain sticky and rough. Don't overwork it or the bread will be tough. If too crumbly, add more buttermilk or fromage frais, if too wet, add more flour.

4   Form the dough into a plump round loaf and place it on a lightly floured, non-stick baking tray. Cut a shallow cross in the top. Bake in the oven for 35–40 minutes. When done, it will sound hollow when tapped on the bottom. Cool on a rack.

 # CHEESE SCONES

Yields 9 scones

35–40 minutes

Split and toasted, cheese scones are a great treat.

---

1 lb/450 g white self-raising flour	½–¾ pt/300–400 ml buttermilk
2 pinches salt	(or 9 fl oz/275 ml fromage frais
Freshly ground pepper to taste (be	thinned with 6 fl oz/175 ml
generous)	skimmed milk)
6 tablespoons grated Parmesan	
cheese	

---

1   Preheat the oven to 400°F, 200°C, Gas Mark 6.

2   Put the flour in a large bowl. Sprinkle the salt, pepper and cheese all over it. Lightly mix with your hand. Make a well in the middle of the flour.

3   Pour ½ pt/300 ml buttermilk (or thinned fromage frais) into the well. With a wooden spoon, stir the flour into the buttermilk. Add more buttermilk or fromage frais as needed to form a rather rough, slightly sticky dough that forms into a cohesive mass. Knead the dough lightly for a few turns. The dough should remain sticky and rough. Don't overwork it or the scones will be tough. If too crumbly, add more buttermilk or fromage frais; if too wet, add flour.

4   Pull 8–9 lumps of dough and form into rough balls about the size of tennis balls. If they are hard to handle because they are so sticky, dip lightly into flour, but be careful to treat them gently so they will not be tough. Again don't overwork them – they don't have to be perfectly round. Sprinkle a non-stick baking tray with flour. Evenly space the balls out. Bake

in the oven for 30–35 minutes. When they are done, they will sound hollow when tapped on the bottom. Cool on a rack.

♀ ❄ GARLIC, SUN-DRIED TOMATO BREAD

Yields 1 loaf

⏱ 45–50 minutes

An infusion of garlic, minced sun-dried tomatoes and fennel seeds added to the basic soda-bread recipe produces a very elegant and spicy loaf. On the next day, if there is any left over, slice it, lay a piece of medium-fat mozzarella on each slice and grill until the cheese is melted and lightly speckled with brown. Do I need to tell you how good it is?

---

4 cloves garlic crushed
5–6 sun-dried tomatoes, diced (use scissors)
1½ tablespoons fennel seeds – optional
½ pt/300 ml stock
8 oz/225 g white self-raising sponge flour
8 oz/225 g brown self-raising sponge flour

Salt
6 tablespoons grated Parmesan cheese
½–¾ pt/300–400 ml buttermilk (or 9 fl oz/275 ml fromage frais thinned with 6 fl oz/175 ml skimmed milk)

---

1 Preheat the oven to 400°F, 200°C, Gas Mark 6.
2 Combine the garlic, sun-dried tomatoes, fennel seeds and stock in a heavy bottomed frying pan. Cover and bring to the boil. Boil for 7 minutes. Uncover and simmer until the garlic and tomatoes are tender and the liquid has cooked down to a syrupy glaze.
3 Combine the flours and salt in a large bowl. Sprinkle on the cheese. Mix with your hand. Add the garlic mixture to the flour. Make a well in the middle of the flour. Pour ½ pt/ 300 ml of buttermilk (or thinned fromage frais) into the well.
4 With a wooden spoon, stir the flour into the buttermilk. When the mixture forms a cohesive mass, knead it a few turns, right in the bowl. If the dough is too crumbly, add a bit more buttermilk, if too wet, a bit more flour, but it should remain slightly sticky.
5 Form the dough into a plump round and place it on a lightly floured non-stick baking tray. With a sharp knife, cut a

shallow cross on the top. Bake for 35–40 minutes. When done, it will sound hollow when tapped on the bottom, and it will be beautifully browned. Cool on a rack.

❄ HAM AND CHEESE BREAD

Yields 1 large loaf

🕒 40–45 minutes

You might call this loaf a picnic bread; the ham, cheese and mustard are all baked right into the loaf.

---

1 lb/450 g self-raising sponge flour
Freshly ground pepper to taste
6 tablespoons grated Parmesan
* cheese*
4 oz/110/g Parma ham, trimmed of
* all fat, and minced fine*

2 tablespoons Dijon mustard
Approx ¾ pt/400 ml buttermilk (or
* 10 fl oz/300 ml fromage frais*
* thinned with 5 fl oz/150 ml*
* skimmed milk)*

---

1   Preheat the oven to 400°F, 200°C, Gas Mark 6.
2   Put the flour in a large bowl. Sprinkle the pepper, cheese and minced Parma ham over it. Lightly mix with your hand. Make a well in the middle of the flour.
3   Whisk together the mustard and ½ pt/300 ml buttermilk (or fromage frais). Pour the mustard-buttermilk mixture into the well. With a wooden spoon, stir the flour into the buttermilk. Mix to form a rather rough, slightly sticky dough that forms a cohesive mass. Lightly knead it for a few turns, right in the bowl. Add more flour if it is too wet, or more buttermilk if it is too crumbly, but remember that the dough should remain slightly sticky. Don't overwork it or the dough will be tough.
4   Form the dough into a plump round loaf and place on a non-stick baking tray that has been sprinkled with flour. With a sharp knife, cut a shallow cross on the top of the loaf. Bake in the oven for 35–40 minutes. When done, it will be browned and crusty and will sound hollow when tapped on the bottom. Cool on a rack.

CORN BREAD

Yields 1 large loaf

⏱ 40–45 minutes

I often find myself combining culinary traditions. The pumper-nickel bread on page 144 for instance merges Ireland and Eastern Europe. Here, Irish bread-baking cozies up to that of the South-western United States. Canned creamed corn forms part of the liquid ingredients so the finished bread is studded, here and there, with kernels of sweetcorn. Corn (maize) meal replaces some of the flour to give a lovely golden colour and additional corn flavour. This is a very special bread.

---

11 oz/300 g white self-raising flour
5 oz/150 g maize meal or polenta
  (coarse maize meal) (see Mail
  Order Guide, page 191)
2 pinches salt
Freshly ground pepper to taste (be
  generous)
6 tablespoons grated Parmesan
  cheese

1 can (10½ oz/285 g) creamed
  corn, poured into a measuring
  jug plus enough buttermilk (or
  fromage frais thinned with
  skimmed milk) to measure
  ¾ pt/400 ml in total
Sprinkling of polenta (maize meal)

---

1 Preheat the oven to 400°F, 200°C, Gas Mark 6.
2 Put the flour and maize meal in a large bowl. Sprinkle the salt, pepper and cheese over it. Lightly mix with your hand. Make a well in the middle of the flour.
3 Pour ½ pt/300 ml of the creamed corn-buttermilk mixture into the well. With a wooden spoon, stir the flour into the buttermilk. Mix to form a rather rough, slightly sticky dough that forms a cohesive mass. Lightly knead it for a few turns, right in the bowl. Add more flour if it is too wet, or more buttermilk if it is too crumbly, but remember that the dough should remain slightly sticky. Don't overwork it or the dough will be tough.
4 Form the dough into a plump round loaf and place on a non-stick baking tray that has been sprinkled with maize meal. With a very sharp knife, cut a shallow cross on the top of the loaf. Bake in the oven for 35–40 minutes. When done, it will be browned and crusty and will sound hollow when tapped on the bottom. Cool on a rack.

♡ 〖 ❊ CHIVE AND MUSTARD-SEED BREAD

Yields 1 large loaf

🕐 40–45 minutes

I like what happens to the basic loaf when Dijon mustard is blended into the dough. The crumb takes on a velvety texture and the taste of the mustard is subtle but not particularly 'hot'. Mustard seeds add more texture, and fresh chives give it a green-flecked, gentle oniony character.

---

8 oz/225 g white self-raising sponge flour	6 tablespoons snipped chives
8 oz/225 g brown self-raising sponge flour	2 tablespoons Dijon mustard
Pinch salt	Approx ¾ pt/400 ml buttermilk (or 10 fl oz/300 ml fromage frais thinned with 5 fl oz/150 ml skimmed milk)
2–2½ tablespoons mustard seeds	

---

1 Preheat the oven to 400°F, 200°C, Gas Mark 6.
2 Put the flours into a large bowl. Sprinkle the salt, mustard seeds and chopped chives over it. Lightly mix with your hand. Make a well in the middle of the flour.
3 Whisk together the mustard and ½ pt/300 ml buttermilk (or thinned fromage frais). Pour the mustard–buttermilk mixture into the well. With a wooden spoon, stir the flour into the buttermilk. Mix to form a rather rough, slightly sticky dough that forms a cohesive mass. Lightly knead it for a few turns, right in the bowl. Add more flour if it is too wet, or more buttermilk if it is too crumbly, but remember that the dough should remain slightly sticky. Don't overwork it or the dough will be tough.
4 Form the dough into a plump round loaf and place on a non-stick baking tray that has been sprinkled with flour. With a very sharp knife, cut a shallow cross on the top of the loaf. Bake in the oven for 35–40 minutes. When done, it will be browned and crusty and will sound hollow when tapped on the bottom. Cool on a rack.

RAISIN BREAD

Yields 1 loaf

⏱ 45–50 minutes

Simmer raisins or sultanas in water along with lemon and orange zest, until the dried fruit is plump and fragrant. Add them to Honey Wheaten bread dough to produce an exquisite breakfast or tea bread. As always, left-overs make wonderful toast, but in order to have left-overs, you'll have to hide the loaf.

---

2 fl oz/50 ml orange juice	*Pinch salt*
2 fl oz/50 ml water	*½–¾ pt/300–400 ml buttermilk*
4 oz/110 g raisins or sultanas	*(or 9 fl oz/275 ml fromage frais*
Slivered zest of ½ lemon	*thinned with 6 fl oz/175 ml*
Slivered zest of ½ orange	*skimmed milk)*
8 oz/225 g white self-raising	*2 tablespoons runny mild honey*
sponge flour	
8 oz/225 g brown self-raising	
sponge flour	

---

1 Preheat the oven to 400°F, 200°C, Gas Mark 6.
2 Combine the juice, water, raisins and citrus zest in a small frying pan. Simmer, until the raisins are plump and have absorbed the liquid.
3 Combine the flours and salt in a large bowl. Sprinkle the raisin mixture over the flour. Make a well in the middle of the flour. Pour ½ pt/300 ml buttermilk (or thinned fromage frais) into the well.
4 With a wooden spoon, stir the flour into the buttermilk. Add the honey and continue stirring. When the liquid forms a cohesive mass, knead it a few turns, right in the bowl. If the dough is too crumbly, add a bit more buttermilk; if too wet, a bit more flour, but it should remain slightly sticky.
5 Form the dough into a plump round loaf and place it on a lightly floured non-stick baking tray. With a sharp knife, cut a shallow cross on the top. Bake for 35–40 minutes. When done, it will sound hollow when tapped on the bottom and it will be beautifully browned. Cool on a rack.

RAISIN SCONES

Yields 9 scones

🕐 35–40 minutes

---

2 fl oz/50 ml orange juice	Pinch salt
2 fl oz/50 ml water	½–¾ pt/300–400 ml buttermilk
4 oz/110 g raisins or sultanas	(or 9 fl oz/275 ml fromage frais
Slivered zest of ½ lemon	thinned with 6 fl oz/175 ml
Slivered zest of ½ orange	skimmed milk)
8 oz/225 g white self-raising	2 tablespoons runny mild honey
sponge flour	
8 oz/225 g brown self-raising	
sponge flour	

---

1   Preheat the oven to 400°F, 200°C, Gas Mark 6.
2   Combine the juice, water, raisins and citrus zest in a small frying pan. Simmer, until the raisins are plump and have absorbed the liquid.
3   Combine the flours and salt in a large bowl. Sprinkle the raisin mixture over the flour. Make a well in the middle of the flour. Pour ½ pt/300 ml buttermilk (or thinned fromage frais) into the well.
4   With a wooden spoon, stir the flour into the buttermilk. Add the honey and continue stirring. When the liquid forms a cohesive mass, knead it a few turns, right in the bowl. If the dough is too crumbly, add a bit more buttermilk; if too wet, a bit more flour, it should remain slightly sticky.
5   Separate into 9 lumps of dough and form into rough balls about the size of tennis balls. If they are hard to handle because they are too sticky, dip lightly into flour, but be careful to treat them gently so they will not be tough. Again, don't overwork them; they should be uneven lumps as opposed to perfect spheres. Sprinkle a non-stick baking tray with flour. Evenly space the balls on the tray. Bake in the oven for 30–35 minutes. When they are done, they sound hollow when tapped on the bottom and a cake tester will emerge clean. Cool on a rack.

FRUIT SCONES

Yields approx 9 scones

🕐 35–40 minutes

Knead some Instant, No-Fat Mincemeat (see page 154) into white-flour soda-bread dough, and you can have fruit scones for tea. Serve them halved, and topped with clouds of Honeyed Vanilla Cream (see page 158).

---

1 lb/450 g self-raising sponge flour
Pinch salt
½–1 pt/300–570 ml buttermilk (or
  9 fl oz/275 ml fromage frais
  thinned with 6 fl oz/175 ml
  skimmed milk)

2 tablespoons runny mild honey
6 oz/175 g Instant, No-Fat
  Mincemeat
Brown sugar – optional
Ground cinnamon – optional

---

1   Preheat the oven to 400°F, 200°C, Gas Mark 6.
2   Put the flour into a large bowl. Sprinkle the salt over it. Lightly mix with your hand. Make a well in the middle of the flour.
3   Pour ½ pt/300 ml buttermilk (or thinned fromage frais) into the well. With a wooden spoon, stir the flour into the buttermilk. Add the honey and more buttermilk or more flour as needed to form a rather rough, slightly sticky dough. Add the mincemeat. Switch from the spoon to both hands and knead for a few turns, right in the bowl. The dough should remain slightly sticky. Don't overwork it or the scones will be tough.
5   Separate into approximately 9 lumps of dough and form into rough balls about the size of tennis balls. If they are hard to handle because they are so sticky, dip lightly into flour, but be careful to treat them gently so they will not be tough. Don't overwork them; they should be uneven lumps as opposed to perfect spheres. Lightly sprinkle a non-stick baking tray with flour. Evenly space the balls on the tray. If you wish, sprinkle each ball with a pinch of brown sugar and cinnamon. Bake for 30–35 minutes. When they are done, they sound hollow when tapped on the bottom and a cake tester will emerge clean. Cool on a rack.

⚱🍶 ✂ INSTANT, NO-FAT MINCEMEAT

Yields 2½ pts/1.4 l

⏱ 9 minutes

With the use of a microwave, Slim Cuisine Mincemeat takes 9 minutes all told: 4 minutes cooking time, 5 minutes standing time. It will keep for several weeks in the fridge. It never pays to make a small batch of such a useful mixture. The recipe yields 2½ pts/1.4 l – with such bounty waiting in the fridge, you can make Fruit Scones (see page 153), Val Kent's Quick Fruit Bread (see page 158) or Mince Pies (see page 184) whenever the mince muse strikes.

---

1 packet (18 oz/500 g) cake fruit (finely minced mixed dried fruit); the mix you choose should include sultanas, currants, orange and lemon peel
1 packet (9 oz/250 g) dried apricots, coarsely chopped (use scissors)

1 packet (5 oz/150 g) dried apple or dried pears, coarsely chopped (use scissors)
½ teaspoon each: ground cinnamon, allspice and nutmeg
2 fl oz/50 ml each: medium sherry and brandy
4 fl oz/110 ml water

---

1 Combine all the ingredients and mix well.
2 Pour in a 4 pint/2.3 l soufflé dish. Cover with microwave cling film and microwave on high for 4 minutes, stirring once halfway through. Pierce the cling film to release the steam, then remove the film. Stir up the mincemeat and allow to stand for 5 minutes. Store, well covered, in the refrigerator.

CITRUS-SCENTED COFFEE CAKE

Makes 1 11-inch/28-cm cake

⏱ 30 minutes

The soda-bread dough used for the scones is very versatile. Try this lemon-coffee cake, or the poppy-seed loaf, and the cranberry- or blueberry-studded breads that follow.

---

1 lb/450 g white self-raising flour
½ teaspoon ground cinnamon
⅛ teaspoon ground mace
1 teaspoon baking soda
Pinch salt
Slivered zest of 1 orange and 1 lemon
½–¾ pt/300–350 ml non-fat

buttermilk (or 9 fl oz/275 ml fromage frais thinned with 6 fl oz/175 ml skimmed milk)
2 tablespoons mild honey
1 teaspoon natural vanilla essence
½ teaspoon each: natural lemon essence and natural orange essence

---

154

1   Preheat the oven to 400°F, 200°C, Gas Mark 6.
2   Sift the flour, spices, soda and salt into a big bowl.
3   Make a well in the flour. Scatter the zests over the flour. Pour 8 fl oz/225 ml buttermilk into the well and drizzle the honey over the buttermilk. Add the essences. With a wooden spoon, gently stir the flour into the buttermilk. When the mixture forms large flakes, use your hands to work it very gently into a cohesive but rough mass. Don't overwork it. When it begins to hold together in an untidy dough, it is ready. Add more buttermilk if the dough is too crumbly, more flour if too wet, but it should be a bit sticky.
4   Lightly flour your hands and your work surface. Form the dough into a rough ball and flatten it. Roll it into a circle (it doesn't have to be a perfect circle) that will fit into an 11-inch/28-cm, non-stick, fluted-edge flan tin. Lightly flour the top of the circle, and fold it into quarters. (Use a long flexible spatula to slip under the dough and fold it over.) Centre the dough in the tin and unfold. Build up the edges and press them against the edge of the tin to flute.
5   Bake for 20–25 minutes, until risen, lightly browned and done. To test for doneness, carefully tip it out of the tin and tap the bottom. It should sound hollow. Cool on a rack. (This cake is delicious both slightly warm and thoroughly cooled.) Serve topped with Honeyed Vanilla Cream (page 158) and cubed fresh fruit, berries, or Fruit Compôte.

Variation:

POPPY-SEED BREAD
1   Omit the zests, spices and lemon and orange essence. Add 4 tablespoons poppy seeds to the flour. Lightly knead the dough for 3–4 turns, right in the bowl.
2   Pat and shape the dough into a loaf shape that will fit into a non-stick bread tin. Put the dough into the tin. Bake for 35–40 minutes until risen, and well browned. When it is done, it sounds hollow when knuckle-thumped on the bottom.

CRANBERRY-NUT BREAD

1 Omit the zests, spices and lemon and orange essence.
2 Mix ¾ pt/400 ml cranberries (frozen cranberries work fine –
   do not thaw them) with 2 tablespoons orange marmalade.
   Add the cranberries to the flour after it has been sifted into
   the bowl in step 2. Sprinkle on 2 oz/50 g pine nuts.
3 In step 3, when the dough comes together in a mass, knead it
   very slightly for 3–4 turns, right in the bowl. Line a baking
   sheet with baking parchment. Form the dough into a plump
   round and centre it on the sheet. If it is hard to handle
   because it is too sticky, dust it and your hands with a bit of
   flour. Cut a cross on the top of the loaf. Bake at 350°F, 180°C,
   Gas mark 4 for 50–60 minutes until done. A knuckle-thump
   on the bottom will sound hollow, and a cake tester will
   emerge clean. Cool on a rack.

Variation:

BLUEBERRY BREAD

Substitute blueberries and lemon marmalade for the cranberries
and orange marmalade in the previous variation. Omit the pine
nuts.

INDIVIDUAL CHOCOLATE BREADS

Yields 8 small loaves

🕐 30–35 minutes

These adorable little loaves are meant to be served one per person.
Make sure that each person has a small serrated knife (a steak knife
is perfect), because the breads are meant to be cut into slices, just
like a large loaf. Serve chocolate breads, along with individual pots
of interesting spreads, for tea, for breakfast or for a truly sybaritic
snack. What to spread on a slice of chocolate bread? Try Chocolate Butter or Mocha-Cinnamon Butter (see pages 182 and 183),
Fig Butter or Prune Butter (see pages 177 and 178) or low-sugar
cherry jam, along with Honey Vanilla Cream (see page 158).

---

1 lb/450 g white self-raising sponge flour	¾–1 pt/400–570 ml buttermilk (or 5 fl oz/150 ml fromage frais thinned with 6 fl oz/175 ml skimmed milk)
3 oz/75 g sifted low fat, unsweetened cocoa powder	
Pinch salt	4 tablespoons runny honey

---

1   Preheat the oven to 400°F, 200°C, Gas Mark 6.
2   Sift the flour, cocoa and salt into a large bowl. Make a well in the middle of the flour.
3   Pour ¾ pt/400 ml buttermilk (or thinned fromage frais) into the well. With a wooden spoon, stir the flour into the buttermilk. Add the honey and more buttermilk as needed to form a rather rough, slightly sticky dough. Switch from the spoon to both hands, and knead for a few turns, right in the bowl. Add more flour if too wet, more buttermilk if too crumbly, but the dough should remain slightly sticky. Don't overwork it or the bread will be tough.
4   Pull off 8 lumps of dough and form into rough balls a little larger than tennis balls. If they are hard to handle because they are so sticky dip lightly into flour, but be careful to treat them gently so they will not be tough. Again, don't overwork them. Sprinkle a non-stick baking tray with flour. Evenly space the balls on the tray. Bake in the oven for 20–30 minutes. When they are done, they sound hollow when tapped on the bottom, and a toothpick will emerge clean. Cool on a rack.

Variation:

 CHOCOLATE SCONES

Yields approx 12 scones

25–30 minutes

How can I say which is better, chocolate bread or chocolate scones? Each in its own way provides much pleasure. The scones have a very tender texture and are meant to be split and then topped with something wonderful. I would opt for Honeyed Vanilla Cream (see page 158) and fresh raspberries or fresh halved and stoned cherries. If anyone you know *still* believes that low-fat food has nothing to do with gastronomic hedonism and delight, feed them these little beauties with the full honeyed-cream-and-raspberry treatment; then sit back and enjoy your triumph.

Make up the dough for chocolate bread (see above), but just mix the dough thoroughly with a wooden spoon; don't knead it. The dough should be on the wet-and-sticky side so add a bit more buttermilk or thinned fromage frais if it seems too dry. With an ice-cream scoop, scoop up portions of the dough and place on a floured non-stick baking tray. Bake for 20–25 minutes. When they are done, a toothpick will emerge clean. Cool on a rack.

HONEYED VANILLA CREAM

Yields 18 fl oz/500 ml

🕐 5 minutes

---

1 vanilla pod	1 lb 2 oz/500 g very low-fat
2 tablespoons runny mild honey	fromage frais

---

1   With a small, sharp knife, split the vanilla pod lengthwise. With the tip of the knife, scrape out the soft pulpy inside from both halves. Scrape the pulp into the fromage frais. (Save the scraped pod to store in a jar of granulated Nutra-Sweet or a canister of castor sugar. It will impart its fragrance to the sweetener.)
2   Add the honey to the fromage frais, and stir so that the black vanilla-bean specks are evenly distributed through the fromage frais. Store in the refrigerator.

❄ VAL KENT'S QUICK FRUIT BREAD

Yields 1 large loaf

🕐 55 minutes

Val Kent bakes fresh yeast bread for her family every morning, and she does it – from start to finish – in less than an hour. When she told me about it, I was very impressed – a loaf of yeast dough usually takes hours longer. Val mixes the dough in a food processor (with the steel S-shaped blade) until it forms a ball of dough, then lets it rise while the oven preheats. She adds Slim Cuisine Mincemeat to the dough which gives the bread character. The problem with baking yeast bread so fast is that it is almost impossible to develop depth of flavour in such a short time; the mincemeat adds a needed dimension. This bread keeps well and it toasts like a dream.

½ oz/10 g fresh yeast (see note, page 161)	Pinch salt
½ pt/300 ml warm water (see note, page 161)	7 oz/200 g Instant, No-Fat Mincemeat (see page 154)
9 oz/250 g strong white flour	Skimmed milk for brushing
9 oz/250 g strong stone-ground wholemeal flour	

---

1   Place the yeast in a measuring jug and cover with 5 fl oz/ 150 ml warm water. Leave to dissolve. Meanwhile put the white and wholemeal flour and a pinch of salt into the bowl of a food processor with the steel blade in place.

2   With a tiny whisk or a fork stir the yeast and water to dissolve the yeast completely. Make up to ½ pt/300 ml with the remaining warm water. Turn the food processor on and add the yeast mixture through the funnel of the lid of the processor. Process in short bursts, stopping to scrape the mixture down occasionally.

3   Add the mincemeat and process until thoroughly blended and a ball of rough dough forms (the mincemeat will almost be puréed into the dough). The whole process takes only a few minutes. Gather up the dough and knead it briefly.

4   Preheat the oven to 450°F, 230°C, Gas Mark 8.

5   Transfer the dough to a large, lightly floured bowl and cover loosely with cling film. Leave the bowl next to the heating oven. When the dough has risen (approximately 20 minutes), form into a loaf shape and place into a non-stick bread tin (see note page 161). Brush with skimmed milk.

6   Bake in the preheated oven for 30 minutes. It is done when it is well browned, and when you rap its bottom with your knuckles it should sound hollow. When done, remove it from the tray (loosen around the sides with a palette knife if necessary and knock it out) and cool on a rack.

To Store One of Your Home-made Loaves:

Do not wrap in cling film or plastic bags; wrapping in plastic bags makes the crust flabby. Leave in a cool part of the kitchen with a piece of cling film against the cut end or store in a paper bag.

♡ ⏃ ❄ QUICK BROWN YEAST BREAD

🕐 60 minutes

Val's recipe set me experimenting with quick yeast breads and I have modified her recipe somewhat to produce a crunchy crusted loaf with a close-grained, tender crumb, that slices beautifully. As with Val's loaf, in the interest of time, you must dispense with hard kneading, multiple risings and so on, so the bread will never have the character of a *slow* yeast bread and you miss the fun of going through the entire ritual. But this makes a very decent loaf of bread (in fact, I find it hard to believe how good it really is) and – on busy days – it pays to be speedy.

½ oz/10 g fresh yeast (see note, page 161)
½ pt/300 ml warm water (see note, page 161)
1 generous teaspoon runny mild honey
9 oz/250 g stone-ground wholemeal flour (see note page 161)
9 oz/250 g strong white flour (see note page 161)
4 tablespoons skimmed milk powder
½ teaspoon salt
Skimmed milk for brushing
Seeds for topping: choose from caraway, fennel, anise, poppy or sesame

1   Place the yeast in a measuring jug. Combine the water and the honey and mix well. Pour 5 fl oz/150 ml of the warm honey water over the yeast and stir with a fork or tiny whisk.
2   Put the flours, milk powder and salt in the processor container that has been fitted with the steel S-shaped blade.
3   Pour remaining water into the yeast mixture to make up to ½ pt/300 ml. Turn on the processor. Pour the yeast mixture in through the feed tube. Process until a ball of dough is formed. This takes a few minutes. Sometimes, some of the mixture gets stuck under the blade and the machine stops before the dough has properly formed. In such cases, pull up the blade, clear the flour mixture out of the way, then start the machine again.
4   Bring the kettle to the boil. Put a roasting tin or Corning Ware 10-inch/25.5-cm square, 2-inch/5-cm deep casserole on the bottom of the *cold* oven and pour in the boiling water. Do not turn the oven on. Gather up the dough and knead it briefly, forming it into a ball. Put it into a large lightly floured bowl and cover loosely with cling film. Put the bowl into the steamy oven and let the dough rise for half an hour.
5   Remove the dough from the oven, and knead it a few turns to knock it down. Nudge, cajole, pat and shape the dough into a loaf shape and put it into a non-stick loaf tin (see note, page 161). (Alternatively, form it into a bloomer shape, cut three evenly spaced shallow slashes across the top and put it on a flour-sprinkled baking tray.) Remove the water-filled roasting pan from the oven.
6   Brush the top with skimmed milk, and sprinkle on the seeds of your choice. Put the tray in the oven, set the oven for 400°F, 200°C, Gas Mark 6, and bake for 25–35 minutes. It is done when it is beautifully browned and glossy, it smells wonderful, and when you tap the bottom of the loaf with

Comfort a scholar with a sustaining and delicious supper in the study:
clockwise from upper right: pan-braised chicken with apples and spiced
carrots; purée of pea soup; and a seductive 'puddle' cake (chocolate torte
with chocolate sauce) garnished with honey-vanilla cream.

What could be cosier than a warming winter supper by a blazing fire?
Clockwise from bottom right: smoky potato-chick pea soup; cheese
bread; piperade pork steaks with tomato-pepper conserve and
cauliflower cheese; citrus fruit on toast with berry sauce.

your knuckles, it sounds hollow. (If a little voice says 'Come in', go and lie down.) When done, remove from the pan (loosen around the sides with a palette knife if necessary, and knock it out) and cool on a rack. This bread is delicious warm or thoroughly cooled. It keeps well: it tastes good on the second and third day, too.

A Note About Yeast

1   If the water is too hot, it will kill the yeast, too cold, and the yeast will go to sleep – 100–108°F 38–42°C is about right. If the water feels *comfortably* warm on your wrist (not too hot, not too cold, not neutral – just comfortably warm) it's just right.
2   Fresh yeast can be purchased from your local bakery. An ounce/25 g, as of writing, costs approximately 12p, and most bakeries will sell you an ounce or two (or more, if you want it). Store it, well covered, in the refrigerator.

A Note About Flour

Once, I wanted to bake some bread, but when I checked the store cupboard, I was out of strong white flour, and stone-ground wholewheat flour, the hard-wheat flours usually used for yeast bread-baking. I decided to bake it anyway, with the only flours I had left: self-raising sponge flour (soft-wheat flour) and superfine self-raising wholemeal flour. To my surprise, the loaf turned out to be very good: it rose like a dream, the crumb was fine grained and tender, it sliced beautifully and the flavour was superb. So, if you don't have strong flour on hand, don't worry; soft flour can be used if it's all that's left in your store cupboard.

A Note About Salt

I use fine-ground seasalt for bread-baking. Salt inhibits the action of yeast, so with such a short rising time, it's best not to use more than the small amount of salt that is specified in the recipe.

A Note About Bread Tins

Both the yeast fruit bread and the yeast brown bread may be baked in either a 1 lb/450 g or a 2 lb/900 g non-stick bread tin. With a 1 lb/450 g tin, the dough will billow up as it bakes to form a beautiful, domed loaf. The loaf baked in a 2 lb/900 g tin will be neater and more compact looking. Either way, when you brush the unbaked loaf with milk, be careful not to let it drip down the sides or the loaf may stick to the tin. When the bread is finished, unmould it from the tin by loosening all around with a palette knife, then turning the tin and shaking or knocking the loaf out. The last few minutes of baking can be done out of the tin, directly on the oven shelf.

♡ 🥕 ❄ QUICK WHITE YEAST BREAD

🕐 60 minutes

---

18 oz/500 g strong white flour	½ oz/10 g fresh yeast
½ teaspooon salt	Skimmed milk or water for
4 tablespoons skimmed milk powder	brushing
½ pt/300 ml warm water (see note,	Seeds: sesame, poppy, caraway, or
page 161)	anise for sprinkling
1 tablespoon mild runny honey	

---

1 Combine the flour, salt and milk powder in the container of a food processor.
2 Combine the water and honey. With a tiny whisk or a fork stir half the mixture into the yeast. When the yeast has dissolved, stir in the remaining liquid.
3 Turn the processor on and pour the yeast-water mixture through the feed tube in a steady stream. Process until the mixture forms a ball of dough. Stop to scrape down occasionally. If the machine clogs and stops too soon, open it, clean away the dough underneath the blade, and start the machine again. Put the kettle on to boil. Put a roasting pan or 10-inch/25.5-cm square, 2-inch/5-cm deep casserole on the floor of the oven.
4 Remove the dough from the processor and knead it for a few turns. Put it into a lightly floured bowl, cover loosely with cling film and put it into the oven. Do not turn the oven on. Pour the boiling water from the kettle into the roasting pan. Close the oven and leave the dough to rise for 30 minutes.
5 Uncover the bowl and remove the dough. Knead it a few turns to expel the gas. Pat and press it down into a flat oval. Starting with a long edge, roll it into a cylinder. Tuck in the ends. Brush the top with milk or water and sprinkle with seeds.
6 Put the loaf, seam side down, on a lightly floured baking

162

tray. Remove the pan of water from the oven. Put the loaf into the oven and set it to 400°F, 200°C, Gas Mark 6.

7   Bake for 25–35 minutes, until the loaf is golden, fragrant, and sounds hollow when you rap its bottom with your knuckles. Cool on a rack.

INSTANT BREAD DOUGH

There is a wonderful convenience food from France available in the chill cabinet of many large supermarkets: bread dough in tube-like containers. The tubes are labelled '4 baguettes', and the small print declares: 'Ready to bake French White Bread Dough'; but it must be said that the dough produces nothing like true French baguettes. It *is*, however, an incredibly convenient, quite good tasting, no-fat dough, useful for instant pizza, little turnovers and pastry-topping for family-style Meat Pies (see page 49).

To prepare the dough, simply peel the label off the cardboard tube and pop the tube open. The dough immediately billows out (small children love that part). Then, separate the four pieces of dough and bake them in whatever shape you like, on a non-stick baking tray, in a hot oven.

To use for sandwiches: If you bake each piece flat (unrolled) for 12–15 minutes, they turn into puffy, square rolls. With a sharp serrated knife, split them horizontally, but not quite all the way through, so they open like a book. Fill these rolls with Sausage Patties (see page 60 and page 62), sliced Fajitas (see page 51) or Whole Field Mushrooms (see page 106). If you bake them to use with Fajitas, before baking brush the dough with some of the marinade.

To use for Deep-Dish Chicago-Style Pizza: Pop open the tube and unroll the dough but don't separate it. (If you want to make a large pizza, open two or more tubes.) Choose a non-stick, shallow casserole or round shallow baking dish, and pat and stretch the dough to fit. Push the dough up all around the edges to form a raised rim. Bake in a 400°F, 200°C, Gas Mark 6 oven for 10–12 minutes, until puffed and lightly browned. Spread this thick crust with hot instant Tomato Sauce (see page 133), and sprinkle with shredded Italian-style medium-fat mozzarella and freshly ground pepper. Bake for an additional 5–7 minutes, until the cheese has melted. Obviously, you can add sautéed mushrooms, peppers or onions to this.

To make an even quicker pizza, follow the above directions, but spread the sauce and cheese over the dough *before* you bake it. Bake for approximately 15–18 minutes in a 400°F, 200°C, Gas Mark 6 oven, until the edges are browned and puffy, and the cheese thoroughly melted. This version does not have the thick, bready crust of a deep-dish Chicago-style pizza – the crust will be thinner and soggier – but children seem to love it.

To Make Little Turnovers: Unroll the dough and separate it. Put a bit of filling (some sautéed mushrooms for instance, or a piece of mozzarella cheese and a dab of tomato sauce, or some well-seasoned cooked spinach) on each square, fold over and pinch closed. Brush each on top with skimmed milk. Bake on a non-stick flat baking tray in a 400°F, 200°C, Gas Mark 6 oven for approximately 12–15 minutes until puffed and brown.

Desserts

Fasten your seat-belts: this is the chapter that is going to fly you to the moon. There are some seductively delightful shocks and surprises waiting for you in the following pages: be prepared to be overwhelmed. Who says that fat-prone folks have to avoid chocolate, ice cream, cakes and puddings? What utter balderdash! Very low-fat ingredients can be combined in many ways to create spectacular desserts. I've fooled many people with these recipes. 'I thought you never cooked fattening food,' gasped one chocolate-dazed guest as she scooped every vestige of chocolate truffle torte (page 189) from her plate. When I assured her that the torte was not only extremely low in fat, but had only taken me *5 minutes* to make, she assumed that I was a fluent liar. But it's no lie; these recipes are very low in fat, and *very* fast and easy to throw together. How sweet life is!

PINEAPPLE AND RUM TOAST

Serves 4

🕒 10 minutes

Childish and adult at the same time, this very quick-to-make dessert is built on a base of soggy toast (that's the childish part)

165

that has been soaked in a mixture of orange juice, rum (that's the grown-up part), vanilla and lemon. Pineapple slices crown the rummy, disintegrating bread and the juices, cooked down to a syrupy glaze, are drizzled over the whole thing. Many large supermarkets now carry ripe, peeled, cored pineapple, so all you have to do is slice it. In fact, some supermarkets even sell it ready sliced.

---

1 pt/570 ml orange juice
4 fl oz/110 ml dark rum
½ teaspoon natural vanilla essence
Juice of ½ lemon
Grated zest of ½ lemon
Light brown sugar to taste, if
   needed

1 peeled and cored pineapple, sliced
   (8 slices)
4 slices toasted bakery white bread
   or toasted slices of Wheaten
   Bread (see page 142)

---

1   Put the orange juice, rum, vanilla, lemon juice and zest into a non-reactive frying pan. Drain any juices from the pineapple into the pan. Boil rapidly until reduced by almost half, and syrupy. Taste the juices and stir in a bit more sugar if too tart; a bit more lemon juice if too sweet.
2   Have four shallow soup plates waiting. One slice at a time, dredge the toast on both sides in the juice in the frying pan. Place each piece of bread, as it is saturated, in a soup plate.
3   2–4 at a time (depends on the size of your pan), dredge the pineapple slices, on both sides, in the juices. Arrange 2 slices on each piece of bread.
4   Boil down the juices until very thick and syrupy, almost a glaze. Pour some of the syrupy juices over each bowl. Serve at once.

CITRUS FRUIT ON TOAST WITH BERRY SAUCE

Yields 4 pieces

🕐 10 minutes

If you have any left-over home-made Wheaten Bread with Honey (see page 143), use it as the base for this colourful dessert, otherwise use a thick slice of the best bakery bread available. Many supermarkets sell ready-to-eat fresh orange and grapefruit segments, or frozen ones. If you have frozen ones, use them while they are still slightly icy. The scarlet raspberry sauce on the orange segments looks (and tastes) just wonderful.

1 box (12 oz/350 g) frozen raspberries, defrosted	4 slices hot toast
2 tablespoons orange liqueur (Cointreau or Grand Marnier)	2 pts/1.1 l orange and grapefruit sections
3–4 teaspoons runny honey	1–2 teaspoons brown sugar
	Mint leaves – optional

1 Whirl the thawed berries smooth in a blender, then pour them through a sieve to eliminate the seeds.
2 Stir in 1 tablespoon of orange liqueur and 1–2 teaspoons of honey.
3 Mix together the remaining honey and liqueur. With a pastry brush, coat this mixture on to the hot toast.
4 Arrange the citrus fruit sections on the toast. Pour some raspberry sauce over each serving. Sprinkle a pinch of brown sugar evenly over each slice. Decorate with mint leaves if you have them.

Omit the honey, orange liqueur and brown sugar. Sweeten the raspberry sauce with Nutrasweet.

COLD ORANGES WITH HOT SULTANAS
10 minutes

This is a method, rather than a recipe – the amounts of each ingredient depend on how many you plan to feed. Keep fresh, juicy seedless oranges in the freezer as a matter of course, because you'll need semi-frozen oranges here. When the urge to prepare this hot-and-cold extravaganza strikes, put the raisins on to simmer and then pull the oranges out of the freezer. In approximately 10 minutes you will be able to slice the oranges (although they will still be partially frozen) with a sharp, serrated knife (make sure your knife is sharp, grip the orange with an oven glove and work carefully). If, on the other hand, you have no frozen oranges in the freezer, and want to serve this dessert after supper, put the whole oranges in the freezer when you start dinner preparations. When you are ready for them, the oranges will be partly frozen. When sliced, quickly trim the peel and pith from each slice and overlap them on small cold plates. Spoon the hot, syrupy fragrant raisins into the centre of the icy orange slices and serve at *once*.

Fresh orange juice	*Several handfuls of sultanas*
Grated orange zest	*Ice-cold (partially frozen), large*
Grated zest and juice of ½ lime	*juicy seedless oranges*
Bit of Cointreau or Grand Marnier	

1   Combine all the ingredients except the oranges in a frying pan and simmer until the sultanas are plump and coated in a thick syrup.
2   Slice the oranges. Trim the peel and pith from each slice. Arrange overlapping slices on individual serving plates. Pour and scatter some sultanas with their syrup over the plates. Serve at once.

 ## MANGO MOUSSE

Yields 8 fl oz/225 ml

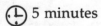 10 minutes

As far as I'm concerned, this serves one. You might try sharing it with a well-loved, mango-craving companion, but both you and your companion will end up eyeing each other's portion with serious larceny in your hearts.

1 whole, ripe mango, peeled and diced (see box, page 127)	*⅛ teaspoon natural vanilla essence*
	¼ teaspoon lime juice
2 tablespoons fromage frais	*Pinch or two NutraSweet to taste*
1 tablespoon buttermilk – optional	

Place all the ingredients into the bowl of a food processor. Blend until smooth. Taste and add more lime juice and/or sweetener. Refrigerate until needed.

 ## ETON MESS

Yields 1¼ pts/700 ml

5 minutes

Strawberries, whipped cream and meringues: an English summer classic, if ever there was one. But once upon a time (perhaps during parents' day at Eton?) some exuberant picnickers must have accidently trodden on the classic, and thus were forced to eat their meringues, strawberries and cream all smashed up into a juicy, scarlet-streaked, crumbly, creamy mishmash. 'What an ungodly mess,' I imagine they cried as they eyed the disaster. 'But how delicious!' they must have exclaimed, as they hungrily lapped up the disaster. And when they were done, I'll bet they licked their fingers contentedly and looked around for more meringues, berries and cream to reduce to a delectable rubble. We should be grateful to those anonymous, clumsy picnickers of long ago – Eton Mess is one of the most satisfying English summer desserts. The Slim Cuisine version retains the delicious messiness of the original, but eliminates the fat Calories.

8 oz/225 g very low-fat fromage frais	*½–1 tablespoon runny mild honey*
Pulp from 1 vanilla pod (see box, page 170), or ½ teaspoon natural vanilla essence	*1 lb/450 g very ripe, flavourful strawberries, hulled*
	1 store-bought meringue shell
	Sprinkle of light brown sugar

1   Whisk together the fromage frais, vanilla pulp and honey.
2   With a potato masher, mash half the strawberries in a bowl until they are a lumpy, juicy purée. Quarter the remaining strawberries.
3   Whisk the purée into the fromage frais. Crumble the meringue. Fold it, along with the strawberry quarters, into the fromage frais mixture. Serve in clear glass goblets or bowls. Top each serving with a sprinkle of brown sugar and allow to stand for a minute or so for the sugar to 'melt'.

STUFFED PEARS

Yields 4 pieces

 10 minutes

These beautiful 'cream'-filled (they're actually quark-filled) pears depend on the pulp of a vanilla bean, or ¼ teaspoon of natural vanilla essence. (See Mail Order Guide page 191 for sources.) When you use the real thing, as opposed to the artificial flavouring, the whole dish becomes imbued with the haunting and exquisite fragrance of the vanilla. Otherwise, the flavour is harsh.

Juice of 1½ oranges	*Pulp of a vanilla bean (see box, page 170), or ¼ teaspoon natural vanilla essence*
2 ripe red pears (or use whatever type of pear is available)	
1 small carton (7 oz/200 g) quark or skimmed milk curd cheese	*2 Amaretti biscuits*
Vanilla NutraSweet to taste (see box, page 170)	

1   Squeeze the juice of 1 orange into a bowl.
2   Peel the pears, halve them and dredge them thoroughly in the orange juice. With a spoon remove the core, leaving a hollow. Dredge the hollow in the juice to prevent browning.
3   Combine the quark, remaining orange juice, NutraSweet and vanilla pulp or vanilla essence in the food processor. Process until very smooth and fluffy.
4   Fill the hollows of the pear halves with the creamy mixture. Crumble the Amaretti and sprinkle evenly over each cream-filled hollow. Serve at once.

♡   Omit Amaretti biscuits

The *Real* Thing

A vanilla bean (it is actually the fruit of an orchid – the *Vanilla Planifolia*) is a long, thin black pod. If you have trouble finding natural vanilla essence, buy a vanilla bean instead. Many supermarkets carry them, one to a jar, on their herb and spice shelves. With a sharp paring knife, slit the pod open lengthwise, then use the tip of the knife to scrape out the pulp. Mix the pulp into the quark (or mix it into fromage frais if you want Honeyed Vanilla Cream, page 158) to imbue it with the vanilla fragrance. Don't discard the scraped-out pod: bury it in a canister of sugar or a jar of granulated NutraSweet. After a few days, the sweetener will become perfumed with vanilla. When the sugar or NutraSweet is gone, save the vanilla pod and bury it in a new jar. It will last for at least a year.

 FRUIT RICOTTA BRULÉE

Serves 8–10

🕐 10 minutes (plus 1 hour chilling time)

Have you seen the exquisite television ads developed for one of the major British supermarkets? A slow, beautifully modulated voice describes a recipe, as the camera, in loving close-up, follows the recipe's languid preparation. Finally, the camera lingers on the owner of the voice – in each case a well-known actor – who smiles beguilingly while holding up a large spoonful of the finished dish, apparently just about to take a nice large bite.

A recent ad in this series follows the preparation of a fruit brulée: perfectly chosen fruit, sliced and arranged in a gratin dish, then blanketed with a thick layer of crème fraîche, sprinkled with soft brown sugar, and briefly grilled until the sugar bubbles. At the end we see a beautiful young woman, slim and radiant, holding a heaped spoonful of this outrageous brulée in front of her smiling lips. Does she *really* eat this stuff, I ask myself? How *can* she, and still look the way she does? I suspect that she (as do I) shuns such unhealthy food. The fruit is fine – it's the crème fraîche that gives me the heebie-jeebies.

At 760 Calories and 80 g of fat per carton, it actually has *more* fat than cream. Why not try the same recipe, with a mixture of quark and low-fat ricotta standing in for the crème fraîche? I think you will be delighted with the results – a symphony of lovely taste and texture – and a study in good nutrition.

---

8 oz/225 g cherries, stoned and
    halved
2 oz/50 g raspberries
8 oz/225 g strawberries, hulled and
    halved
2 peaches, halved, stoned, and
    sliced
8 oz/225 g low-fat ricotta cheese

8 oz/225 g quark
1 heaped tablespoon orange
    marmalade
1 teaspoon natural vanilla essence
1 tablespoon orange liqueur (Grand
    Marnier or Cointreau)
5 tablespoons soft light brown sugar

---

1   Preheat the grill to high.
2   Arrange the fruit in an 8-inch/20.5-cm square, 2-inch/5-cm deep pyrex or pyroflam baking dish. Cover and refrigerate while you prepare the topping.
3   Combine all the remaining ingredients (except the brown sugar) in the container of a food processor. Process until fluffy. Spoon and spread the mixture over the fruit.
4   Sprinkle the brown sugar evenly over the top and smooth with the back of a spoon. Grill, close to the heat, for ½–1 minute until the sugar bubbles. Chill for at least an hour before serving.

PEACH ICE CREAM

Yields 1 pt/570 ml

🕐 5 minutes

I've been making fruit 'ice cream' by this method for years now, in fact it's become a Slim Cuisine trade mark. Even so, it still amazes me. Just whip up some solidly frozen fruit cubes or berries in a processor with buttermilk or fromage frais and NutraSweet and, in scant minutes, the processor container is filled with a creamy, vividly fruit-flavoured ice cream. The recipe below is for my current favourite – fresh peach ice cream, but use this method for any frozen fruit or berries. Since I've never seen frozen peaches in the supermarket, you'll have to think ahead for this one. In season, buy ripe peaches, cut them into cubes (no need to peel them first) and freeze flat on non-stick trays. When they are solidly frozen, gather the pieces up into plastic bags, and keep in the freezer until you are ready to make ice cream. When you are ready to make the ice cream, if the fruit pieces have frozen into a solid block, knock them on the counter a few times to separate them. Once completed, the ice cream may be kept in the freezer for up to an hour. If it stays any longer it freezes solid, and will never regain its creamy glory, even if left to soften. So make it and serve it. The recipe can be cut down if necessary.

12 oz/350 g frozen peach cubes	NutraSweet to taste
6–8 fl oz/175–225 ml buttermilk or fromage frais thinned with a dash of skimmed milk	

1   Dump the fruit, still frozen, into the bowl of a food processor. Pour in half of the buttermilk.
2   Turn on the machine. Blend for a few seconds, stopping to scrape down the sides if necessary. Taste. Add a bit of NutraSweet if needed. Pour in the remaining buttermilk. Process until the mixture forms a super-creamy ice cream. Spoon into clear glass goblets and serve at once.

For a special dinner-party dessert, serve in a store-bought meringue shell, with a crumbled Amaretti biscuit sprinkled on top. To pull out all the stops, add Slim Cuisine Milk Chocolate Sauce (see page 178).

MELON SORBET

Yields approx ½ pt/300 ml

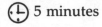 5 minutes

Probably the most refreshing sorbet in the world. Serve it on a hot day, garnished with mint leaves.

1 lb/450 g frozen melon balls	½–1 tablespoon orange liqueur (Cointreau or Grand Marnier) – optional
4–5 fl oz/110–150 ml orange juice	

1   Put the frozen melon balls into the food processor along with 2 fl oz/50 ml orange juice and the orange liqueur, if using.
2   Turn the machine on and allow to process for a few moments – stop and scrape down the sides. Turn it on again and pour the remaining liquid in through the feed tube. Continue processing, stopping to scrape down the sides occasionally until the mixture forms a fluffy sorbet consistency. Serve at once.

♡   Prepare the sorbet without the orange liqueur.

ANGEL BUNS

Yields 24 buns

🕐 20 minutes

Classic Angel Cake batter contains no fat and no whole eggs – only whites. And when you bake an Angel Cake, the baking tin never needs to be greased. If you bake Angel Cake batter in patty tins, these mini Angel Buns will be ready in 15–18 minutes. They – and the chocolate version that follows – are perfect for children's birthday parties.

2 oz/50 g self-raising sponge flour	*Pinch cream of tartar*
1½ oz/40 g castor sugar	*2 oz/50 g castor sugar*
5 egg whites, at room temperature	*1 teaspoon natural vanilla essence*

1   Preheat the oven to 350°F, 180°C, Gas Mark 4.
2   Sift together the flour and 1½ oz/40 g sugar. Set aside.
3   Beat the egg whites until foamy. Add the cream of tartar and beat until they hold soft peaks. Continue beating, adding the remaining 2 oz/50 g sugar, 2 tablespoons at a time, until the sugar is dissolved, and the whites are stiff and glossy. Fold in the vanilla essence.
4   A little at a time, sprinkle the sifted flour/sugar mixture over the batter and fold in gently but thoroughly.
5   Taking 1½ tablespoons at a time, fill two patty tins (12 depressions each).
6   Bake in the oven for 15–18 minutes.
7   Allow to cool on a rack before loosening each bun with a palette knife and then unmoulding.

CHOCOLATE ANGEL BUNS

Yields 24 buns

 20 minutes

Every good baked dessert needs a chocolate variation.

1½ oz/40 g self-raising sponge flour	1½ oz/40 g castor sugar
3 tablespoons low-fat, unsweetened cocoa (see Mail Order Guide page 192)	5 egg whites, at room temperature
	Pinch cream of tartar
	2 oz/50 g castor sugar
	1 teaspoon natural vanilla essence

---

1   Preheat the oven to 350°F, 180°C, Gas Mark 4.
2   Sift together the flour, cocoa and 1½ oz/40 g sugar. Set aside.
3   Beat the egg whites until foamy. Add the cream of tartar and beat until they hold soft peaks. Continue beating, adding the remaining 2 oz/50 g sugar, 2 tablespoons at a time, until the sugar is dissolved, and the whites are stiff and glossy. Fold in the vanilla essence.
4   A little at a time, sprinkle the sifted flour, cocoa and sugar mixture over the batter and fold in gently but thoroughly.
5   Taking 1½ tablespoons at a time, fill two patty tins (12 depressions each).
6   Bake in the oven for 15–18 minutes.
7   Allow to cool on a rack before loosening the buns with a palette knife and unmoulding.

STRAWBERRY JAM FILLED WHITE ANGEL BUNS

25 minutes

Try a fruity variation – a dollop of low-sugar jam baked into the centre of Angel Buns: strawberry for vanilla, cherry for chocolate.

---

2 oz/50 g self-raising sponge flour	2 oz/50 g castor sugar
1½ oz/40 g castor sugar	1 teaspoon natural vanilla essence
5 egg whites, at room temperature	Low-sugar strawberry jam
Pinch cream of tartar	

---

1   Preheat the oven to 350°F, 180°C, Gas Mark 4.
2   Sift together the flour and 1½ oz/40 g sugar. Set aside.
3   Beat the egg whites until foamy. Add the cream of tartar and beat until they hold soft peaks. Continue beating, adding the

remaining 2 oz/50 g sugar, 2 tablespoons at a time, until the sugar is dissolved, and the whites are stiff and glossy. Fold in the vanilla essence.

4   A little at a time, sprinkle the sifted flour/sugar mixture over the batter and fold in gently but thoroughly.

5   Taking 1 tablespoon at a time, fill two patty tins (12 depressions each). Put ½ teaspoon of jam on top of each one. Dollop ½ tablespoon of the batter mixture on top to cover the jam.

6   Bake in the oven for 15–18 minutes.

7   Allow to cool on a rack before loosening the buns with a palette knife and unmoulding.

CHERRY JAM FILLED
CHOCOLATE ANGEL BUNS

25 minutes

1½ oz/40 g self-raising sponge flour	*5 egg whites, at room temperature*
3 tablespoons low-fat, unsweetened cocoa powder (see Mail Order Guide, page 192)	*Pinch cream of tartar*
	2 oz/50 g castor sugar
	1 teaspoon natural vanilla essence
1½ oz/40 g castor sugar	*Low-sugar cherry jam*

---

1   Preheat the oven to 350°F, 180°C, Gas Mark 4.

2   Sift together the flour, cocoa and 1½ oz/40 g sugar. Set aside.

3   Beat the egg whites until foamy. Add the cream of tartar and beat until they hold soft peaks. Continue beating, adding the remaining 2 oz/50 g sugar, 2 tablespoons at a time, until the sugar is dissolved, and the whites are stiff and glossy. Fold in the vanilla essence.

4   A little at a time, sprinkle the sifted flour, cocoa, sugar mixture over the batter and fold in gently but thoroughly.

5   Dollop 1 tablespoon of batter into each section of 2 patty tins. Top each with ½ teaspoon low-sugar cherry jam. Dollop ½ tablespoon of the remaining batter over each to cover the jam.

6   Bake in the oven for 15–18 minutes.

7   Allow to cool on a rack before unmoulding the buns.

SWISS ROLL

25 minutes

Angel Cake batter, white or chocolate, can be baked flat, spread with something wonderful (try Fig Butter, Prune Butter, Chocolate Pudding, Mocha-Cinnamon Pudding, or crushed fresh raspberries folded into Vanilla Pudding) and rolled. To serve, slice the roll and overlap the slices on a platter.

2 oz/50 g self-raising sponge flour	Pinch cream of tartar
1½ oz/40 g castor sugar	2 oz/50 g castor sugar
5 egg whites, at room temperature	1 teaspoon natural vanilla essence

1   Preheat the oven to 350°F, 180°C, Gas Mark 4.
2   Sift together the flour and 1½ oz/40 g sugar. Set aside.
3   Beat the egg whites until foamy. Add the cream of tartar and beat until they hold soft peaks. Continue beating, adding the remaining 2 oz/50 g sugar, 2 tablespoons at a time, until the sugar is dissolved, and the whites are stiff and glossy. Fold in the vanilla essence.
4   A little at a time, sprinkle the sifted flour/sugar mixture over the batter and fold in gently but thoroughly.
5   Spread the mixture on to a silicone paper-lined Swiss roll tin.
6   Bake in the oven for 15–18 minutes.
7   Allow to cool in the pan, on a rack, before peeling the paper off the Swiss roll. Spread a tea-towel on your work surface and turn the cake out on to it. Spread the cake with Fig Butter (see page 177), Prune Butter (see page 177) or Chocolate Butter (see page 182). Start at a long edge and use the towel to help roll the cake. It may crack, but it won't matter – the finished roll will still look just fine and taste glorious. Store the roll, well covered, in the refrigerator.

CHOCOLATE SWISS ROLL

25 minutes

1½ oz/40 g self-raising sponge flour	5 egg whites, at room temperature
3 tablespoons low-fat, unsweetened cocoa powder (see Mail Order Guide, page 192)	Pinch cream of tartar
	2 oz/50 g castor sugar
	1 teaspoon natural vanilla essence

1   Preheat the oven to 350°F, 180°C, Gas Mark 4.
2   Sift together the flour, cocoa, and the 1½ oz/40 g sugar. Set aside.

3   Beat the egg whites until foamy. Add the cream of tartar and beat until they hold soft peaks. Continue beating, adding the remaining 2 oz/50 g sugar, 2 tablespoons at a time, until the sugar is dissolved, and the whites are stiff and glossy. Fold in the vanilla essence.
4   A little at a time, sprinkle the sifted flour, cocoa and sugar mixture over the batter and fold in gently but thoroughly.
5   Spread the mixture on to a silicone paper-lined Swiss roll tin.
6   Bake in the oven for 15–18 minutes.
7   Allow to cool on a rack before peeling the paper off the Swiss roll. Spread a tea-towel on your work surface and turn the cake out on to it. Spread the cake with the filling of your choice (see suggestions, previous recipe). Start at a long edge and use the towel to help roll the cake. It may crack, but it won't matter – the finished roll will still look just fine and taste glorious. Store the roll, well covered, in the refrigerator.

PRUNE 'BUTTER'

Yields approx ½ pt/300 ml

🕐 5 minutes

Prune Butter contains no butter, but it spreads like butter, and will do wonderful things to your breakfast toast or your scones.

1 package (9 oz/250 g) ready-to-eat stoned prunes, diced	*Juice of ¼ lemon*
1 carton (7 oz/200 g) quark or skimmed milk curd cheese	*⅛ teaspoon ground mace*
¼ teaspoon natural vanilla essence	*⅛ teaspoon ground cinnamon*
	⅛ teaspoon ground allspice

1   Put all the ingredients into the bowl of a food processor and blend until smooth. Taste and add in a bit more seasoning if you feel it needs it. Store in the refrigerator until required.

FIG 'BUTTER'

Yields approx ½ pt/300 ml

🕐 5 minutes

When I was a child, my favourite cookie was the Fig Newton. English children like Fig Newtons too, but they call them Fig *Rolls*. Fig Butter (like Prune Butter, it's great on scones and toast) is very reminiscent of the filling in those childhood Fig Newtons (how can you *not* love a cookie with a name like that?) Use Fig Butter to fill a Swiss Roll (see page 176) and you have a low-fat and very sophisticated version of the childhood classic.

---

1 package (9 oz/250 g) ready-to-eat figs	¼ teaspoon natural vanilla essence
1 carton (7 oz/200 g) quark or skimmed milk curd cheese	Sprinkling of granulated NutraSweet, to taste
	Few drops of fresh lemon juice

---

1   Dice the figs. Put them into the container of a food processor with the quark and vanilla essence. Blend until almost smooth.
2   Add NutraSweet to taste (if any is needed at all) and a few drops of fresh lemon juice. Process until perfectly smooth. Taste and add lemon juice and/or NutraSweet if required, then process once more to blend. Store in the refrigerator until needed.

◊ ▯ ▦ MILK CHOCOLATE SAUCE

Yields 1 pt/570 ml

⊕5 minutes

I love deep, dark, bitter-sweet, serious chocolate – the sort that wraps itself around your palate and asserts itself. Sometimes I forget that milk chocolate – a little paler, a little sweeter, a little less bombastic – has a devoted following as well. So here is my offering to the milk chocolate fans; a suave and beautiful hot chocolate sauce meant to be served with Slim Cuisine food processor peach, raspberry or pear ice cream (see page 171). For a quick but impressive party dessert, put a store-bought meringue on a plate, top with a generous scoop of Slim Cuisine Peach Ice Cream (see page 171), dollop the milk chocolate sauce all around it and crumble on a crushed Amaretti biscuit. Eat at once.

---

5 tablespoons low-fat cocoa powder (see Mail Order Guide, page 192)	2 tablespoons cornflour
	1 pt/570 ml skimmed milk
5 tablespoons vanilla sugar	½–1 teaspoon natural vanilla essence
6 tablespoons skimmed milk powder	½–1 tablespoon dark rum

---

1   Sift the dry ingredients into a 3½ pt/2 litre, 7 inch/18 cm top diameter, opaque, white-plastic measuring jug (see box, page 189). Whisk in the milk, vanilla and rum vigorously. Cover the jug tightly with microwave cling film.

2   Microwave on full power for 3 minutes. Uncover (avert your face, and begin with the side *away* from you, to release the steam. Be careful – the steam is hot) and whisk thoroughly. Re-cover and microwave on full power for 2 minutes more. Uncover and whisk again. If the mixture hasn't boiled and thickened by now, microwave for another minute, then whisk again. If necessary, microwave for another ½–1 minute until it has boiled and thickened. Uncover, heat and let stand for 5 minutes, whisking occasionally. Store in the refrigerator with a covering of microwave cling film resting on the surface of the sauce.

VANILLA MILK PUDDING

Yields 1 pt/570 ml

 5 minutes

This makes a trembling, soft, soothing milk pudding.

---

3 tablespoons cornflour	Approx 18 fl oz/500 ml skimmed
5 tablespoons skimmed milk powder	milk (1 longlife carton)
4 tablespoons sugar	
Pulp of 1 vanilla pod (see box, page 170)	

---

1   Sift the cornflour, milk powder, sugar and vanilla pod pulp into a 3½-pt/2 l, 7-inch/18-cm top diameter, opaque white plastic measuring jug (see box, page 189). Use a wooden spoon or rubber spatula to rub the vanilla pulp through the sieve if necessary.
2   With a wire whisk, mix the milk thoroughly into the dry ingredients – you don't want lumps. Also, vigorous whisking helps prevent volcanic eruptions. Cover the jug with microwave cling film.
3   Microwave on full power for 3 minutes. Uncover (avert your face, and begin with the side *away* from you, to release the steam. Be careful – the steam is hot) and whisk briskly. Re-cover and microwave on full power for 2 minutes more. Uncover and whisk again. If the mixture hasn't boiled and thickened by now, microwave for another minute, then whisk again. If necessary, microwave for another ½–1 minute until it has boiled and thickened. Uncover, whisk and allow to stand for 5 minutes, whisking occasionally. Store in the refrigerator, with a covering of microwave cling film resting on the surface of the pudding.

As above, but leave out the sugar. Whisk in granulated Nutra-Sweet to taste after the pudding has cooled (approximately 3–4 tablespoons).

┌───┐
│   **Fruit Puddings**   │
│   **(Mango, Strawberry, etc.)**   │
│ To make a summer fruit milk pudding, purée some fruit │
│ (mangoes, peaches, strawberries, raspberries, plums, etc.) If │
│ the fruit has pips, sieve the pulp. Stir or swirl the pulp into │
│ Vanilla Milk Pudding.   │
└───┘

BANANA MILK PUDDING

Yields 1½ pts/900 ml

🕐 7 minutes

Another childish dessert, that adults seem to adore for its very childishness. 'Nanner pudding' is how they refer to it in some parts of the US.

2 very *ripe bananas, peeled and thickly sliced*	3 tablespoons sugar
½ teaspoon natural vanilla essence	¼ teaspoon each: ground mace, ground cinnamon
3 tablespoons cornflour	Pinch freshly grated nutmeg
5 tablespoons skimmed milk powder	Approx 18 fl oz/500 ml skimmed milk (1 longlife carton)

1 With a potato masher, mash the banana slices and vanilla to a pulp on the bottom of a 3½ pt/2 l, 7-inch/18-cm top diameter, opaque white plastic measuring jug (see box, page 189).
2 Sift the cornflour, milk powder, sugar and spices into the jug.
3 With a wire whisk, mix together the milk, dry ingredients and the banana pulp. Whisk vigorously. Cover the jug with microwave cling film.
4 Microwave on full power for 3 minutes. Uncover (avert your face, and begin with the side *away* from you, to release the steam. Be careful – the steam is hot) and whisk thoroughly. Re-cover and microwave on full power for 2 minutes more. Uncover and whisk once more. If it has not boiled and thickened, cover and microwave for ½–1 minute more.

Uncover and whisk well again. Allow to stand for 5 minutes, whisking occasionally. Store, in the refrigerator, with a covering of microwave cling film resting on the surface of the pudding.

 As above, but leave out the sugar. Whisk in granulated NutraSweet to taste after the pudding has cooled (approx 3–4 tablespoons).

 ## ORANGE MILK PUDDING

Yields 1 pt/570 ml

🕐 5 minutes

Orange liqueur gives milk pudding a much more sophisticated air; it's trembling, soft and all of that, but it has a nice splash of booze to give it zing.

3 tablespoons cornflour	Approx 18 fl oz/500 ml skimmed
5 tablespoons skimmed milk powder	milk (1 longlife carton)
3–4 tablespoons sugar	Juice of ½ large orange
1 tablespoon orange liqueur (Grand Marnier or Cointreau)	

1 Sift the cornflour, milk powder and sugar into a 3½ pt/2 l, 7-inch/18-cm top diameter, opaque white plastic measuring jug (see box, page 189).
2 With a wire whisk, mix the liqueur and milk into the dry ingredients. Whisk well – you don't want lumps. Vigorous whisking helps eliminate volcanic eruptions. Cover the jug with microwave cling film.
3 Microwave on full power for 3 minutes. Uncover (avert your face, and begin with the side *away* from you, to release the steam. Be careful – the steam is hot) and whisk thoroughly. Re-cover and microwave on full power for 2 minutes more. Uncover and whisk again. If the mixture hasn't boiled and thickened by now, microwave for another minute, then whisk again. If necessary, microwave for another ½–1 minute until it has boiled and thickened. Uncover, whisk in the orange juice and allow to stand for 5 minutes, whisking occasionally. Store, in the refrigerator, with a covering of microwave cling film resting on the surface of the pudding.

CHOCOLATE 'BUTTER'

Yields 2 pts/1.1 l

🕐 5 minutes

This makes a thick, rich, fudgy chocolate pudding – sheer heaven for chocoholics. It's called Chocolate Butter, because of its voluptuous spreading consistency. Use it to fill Swiss Rolls (see page 176) and little Tartlet Shells (see page 183) as well as serving it as it is in bowls, to your best chocoholic friends. It also makes a *superb* spread for slices of Chocolate Bread, and split Chocolate Scones (see page 157).

---

9 tablespoons low-fat, unsweetened cocoa (see Mail Order Guide, page 192)
3 tablespoons cornflour
5 tablespoons skimmed milk powder

8 tablespoons sugar
½ teaspoon natural vanilla essence
Approx 18 fl oz/500 ml skimmed milk (1 longlife carton)

---

1 Sift the cocoa, cornflour, milk powder and sugar into a 3½ pt/2 litre, 7-inch/18-cm top diameter, opaque white-plastic measuring jug (see box, page 189).

2 With a wire whisk, whisk the vanilla and milk thoroughly into the dry ingredients – you don't want lumps. Vigorous whisking helps eliminate volcanic eruptions. Cover the jug with microwave cling film.

3 Microwave on full power for 3 minutes. Uncover (avert your face, and begin with the side *away* from you, to release the steam. Be careful – the steam will be hot) and whisk briskly. Re-cover and microwave on full power for 2 minutes more. Uncover and whisk again. If the mixture hasn't boiled and thickened by now, microwave for another minute, then whisk again. If necessary, microwave for another ½–1 minute until it is beautifully thickened. Uncover, whisk and let stand for 5 minutes, whisking occasionally. Store, in the refrigerator, with a covering of microwave cling film resting on the surface of the pudding.

♦ ⊟ ⊠ MOCHA-CINNAMON 'BUTTER'

Yields 2 pts/1.1 l

⊕ 5 minutes

Add a little cinnamon to the basic chocolate-butter recipe and replace some of the milk with cooled strong coffee (*real* coffee, not the awful instant stuff) and you have mocha-cinnamon butter – chocolate with a Mexican accent.

9 tablespoons low-fat, unsweetened cocoa (see Mail Order Guide page 192)	¼–½ teaspoon cinnamon (to taste)
	8 tablespoons sugar
3 tablespoons cornflour	½ teaspoon natural vanilla essence
5 tablespoons skimmed milk powder	12 fl oz/350 ml skimmed milk
	6 fl oz/175 ml cooled coffee

1   Sift the cocoa, cornflour, milk powder, cinnamon and sugar into a 3½ pt/2 l, 7-inch/18-cm top diameter, opaque, white-plastic measuring jug (see box, page 189)
2   With a wire whisk, whisk the vanilla, milk and coffee thoroughly into the dry ingredients – you won't want lumps. Vigorous whisking helps eliminate volcanic eruptions. Cover the jug with microwave cling film.
3   Microwave on full power for 3 minutes. Uncover (avert your face and begin with the side *away* from you, to release the steam. Be careful – the steam is hot) and whisk thoroughly. Re-cover and microwave on full power for 2 minutes more. Uncover and whisk again. If the mixture hasn't boiled and thickened by now, microwave for another minute, then whisk again. If necessary, microwave for another ½–1 minute until it has boiled and thickened. Uncover, whisk and let stand for 5 minutes, whisking occasionally. Store, in the refrigerator, with a covering of microwave cling film resting on the surface of the pudding.

TARTLET SHELLS

Yields 12 shells

⊕ 30 minutes

This is easy, easy, easy (but good, good, good). Just mould slices of crustless bread into the depressions in a bun tin and bake. Brush once with some orange juice. That's it. The resulting little tartlet shells are beguilingly crunchy and make perfect receptacles for dollops of milk puddings – especially the chocolate ones.

What am I saying? The vanilla milk pudding will be perfectly and lovingly encased by these crunchy shells as well. Top each pudding-filled shell with fruit: a raspberry or two for chocolate, slices of strawberry for vanilla, a mandarin slice for orange. Serve them with coffee at the end of a gala dinner.

Top quality sliced bakery bread, white or brown	*3–4 fl oz/75–110 ml fresh orange juice*

1   Preheat oven to 300°F, 150°C, Gas Mark 2.
2   You will need 12 slices. With a 3-inch/7.5-cm diameter drinking glass, cut a circle out of the centre of each slice. Flatten each circle with a rolling pin. Save all trimmings for breadcrumbs, bread puddings, etc.
3   Press a round of bread into each depression in a 12-section bun tin. With your fingers mould it down and up to the sides.
4   Bake for 15 minutes. With a pastry brush, lightly brush the interior of each with orange juice. Remove from the bun tin and bake directly on the oven rack for approximately 10 minutes more, until dried right through. Turn them once or twice during this time. Cool on a rack. Store in an airtight biscuit tin. (They will keep for weeks.)

Christmas Cheer

Make easy, quick mince pies this Christmas by filling tartlet shells with Vanilla Milk Pudding (see page 179) and topping with Instant, No-Fat Mincemeat (see page 154).

 STIR-CRAZY CHOCOLATE TORTE

Makes 1 10-inch/25.5-cm torte

⏲ 20 minutes

I originally wrote about chocolate stir-crazy cakes in *Slim Cuisine: Indulgent Desserts*. For a stir-crazy, you mix a few simple ingredients right in the baking tin, bung it in the oven, and presto: 10–15 minutes later, a perfect, deep-chocolate cake. I received many letters from frustrated chocolate lovers, who were unable to find one of the staple ingredients, buttermilk, in their local supermarket. I have redeveloped the cake therefore to use readily available low-fat fromage frais in place of the elusive buttermilk. This new development is even better than the original – the cake rises to make a lovely chocolate sponge layer. Why not bake two and sandwich them together with Chocolate Butter? (See page 182.)

5½ oz/160 g self-raising sponge flour	Pinch salt
	2 fl oz/50 ml skimmed milk
6 oz/175 g castor sugar	6 fl oz/175 ml low-fat fromage frais
1 oz/25 g unsweetened cocoa	1 teaspoon natural vanilla extract
powder (see Mail Order Guide,	4 fl oz/110 ml water
page 192)	1 tablespoon white vinegar

1   Preheat the oven to 350°F, 180°C, Gas Mark 4.
2   Sift together the flour, sugar, cocoa and salt directly into a 10–11-inch/25–28-cm non-stick flan tin. In a measuring jug, stir the milk into the fromage frais. Add the vanilla extract and pour the liquid over the dry ingredients in the pan.
3   With a wooden spoon, stir the mixture together using a gentle circular motion until the dry ingredients are thoroughly incorporated into the liquid ones. Sprinkle on the vinegar and gently mix it in.
4   Bake for approximately 15 minutes, until *just* done. It will be set and the surface will spring back when lightly pressed. Cool on a rack. Serve warm or at room temperature.

 ## STIR-CRAZY BANANA-FUDGE TORTE

Makes 1 10-inch/25.5-cm torte

⏲ 20 minutes

A banana-flavoured variation of the basic chocolate stir-crazy.

5½ oz/160 g self-raising sponge flour	1 fl oz/25 ml skimmed milk
	3 fl oz/75 ml low-fat fromage frais
4 oz/100 g castor sugar	1 tablespoon white vinegar
1 oz/25 g unsweetened cocoa	1 teaspoon natural vanilla extract
powder (see Mail Order Guide	4 fl oz/110 ml water
page 192)	2 very ripe bananas, peeled and
Pinch salt	mashed to a pulp

1   Preheat oven to 350°F, 180°C, Gas Mark 4.
2   Sift together the flour, sugar, cocoa and salt directly into a 10–11-inch/25–28-cm, non-stick flan tin. In a measuring jug, stir the milk into the fromage frais. Add the vinegar, vanilla extract and water to the fromage frais and pour this liquid over the dry ingredients in the pan. Add the bananas.

3   With a wooden spoon, stir the mixture together using a gentle circular motion until the dry ingredients are thoroughly incorporated into the liquid ones. The mixture will be lumpy from the banana pulp, but that's fine.
4   Bake for approximately 15 minutes, until *just* done. It will be set and the surface will spring back when lightly pressed. If it is allowed to overcook, it will be too dry; it must retain a fudgy texture.
5   Cool on a rack. Serve warm or at room temperature.

STIR-CRAZY CHOCOLATE-CHERRY CAKE

🕐 1 hour

Chocolate, cherries and almond flavouring are brilliant companions. Try them in this open-faced chocolate tart. It's baked in a rectangular baking dish and served cut into squares.

5½ oz/160 g self-raising sponge flour	2 fl oz/50 ml skimmed milk
6 oz/175 g castor sugar	6 fl oz/175 ml fromage frais
1 oz/25 g unsweetened cocoa powder (see Mail Order Guide page 192)	1 tablespoon white vinegar
	1⅕ pts stoned and halved cherries
	3 Amaretti biscuits, crumbled
Pinch salt	1 tablespoon sugar
¼ teaspoon natural almond essence	½ teaspoon natural vanilla essence
4 fl oz/110 ml water	⅛ teaspoon natural almond essence
	Sprinkling of lemon juice

1   Preheat oven to 350°F, 180°F, Gas Mark 4.
2   Sift together the flour, sugar, cocoa and salt into a bowl. In a jug, combine the almond essence, water, skimmed milk, fromage frais and vinegar. Pour the liquid mixture over the dry ingredients in the bowl. With a wooden spoon, stir the mixture together using a gentle circular motion, until the dry ingredients are thoroughly incorporated into the liquid ones.
3   Pour and scrape the batter into a rectangular 13½-inch × 8½-inch/34-cm × 21.5-cm, 2-inch/5-cm deep pyrex baking dish. With a rubber spatula, spread it evenly over the dish.
4   Combine the cherries, Amaretti biscuits, sugar, vanilla essence, almond essence and a sprinkling of lemon juice and pour the mixture in one even layer over the chocolate batter, leaving a ½-inch/1-cm border all around.

5   Bake for approximately 50 minutes. The edges of the cake will be set but not dried out and the surface, when pressed around the edges, will spring back. Cool on a rack. It is best when *thoroughly* cooled. To serve, cut into squares right from the pan.

A Sublime Accident

The next recipe falls into a category of cakes known generically as 'puddle cakes'. Puddle cakes are dense, rich-tasting, intensely chocolaty tortes, baked in a microwave so that they form their own sauce. Where did the concept of puddle cakes originate? The whole thing was a sublime accident. Recipe development can get really frenzied in my kitchen, especially when I'm in the grip of a new technique. Some basic techniques and recipes are so beguiling, so infinitely versatile that my staff and I find ourselves trying them over and over again, changing things here and there, to see how many variations can be played on the basic theme. Not long ago, microwave milk puddings and sauces had me under their spell: by varying the amount of cornflour, the texture changed from sauce, to pudding, to cake filling, and of course infinite flavour changes were possible: fruit, chocolate, vanilla, citrus . . .

One day a chocolate mixture was in its jug in the microwave – the plan was to microwave it for 3 minutes – pull it out, stir it like mad with a whisk to keep it smooth, then return it for another 2–3 minutes. The result was to have been a thick, dark, satiny sauce. The microwave timer was set for 6 minutes; after 3 minutes I meant to pull it out, administer the whisking, and put it back for the final few minutes. But I crossed the kitchen to help my assistant with something else and totally forgot about it. 'Ping' went the microwave timer. We all stopped short. Oops! That's 5 minutes – the sauce must be totally ruined. But when I pulled away the microwave cling film and peered into the jug, the sauce was not ruined – it was *gone*. In its place was what appeared to be some sort of dark chocolate sponge cake. A very slight crack ran across the top of the sponge: gusts of pure, dense chocolate-imbued steam gently wafted up through the crack. My sauce – where was my sauce?

With a long palette knife, I loosened the mysterious chocolate-cake-thing all around its perimeter, put an inverted plate over the top of the jug, and reversed the whole thing. The contents gently slid out. I tossed the jug aside and stared. There on the plate was a dome-shaped chocolate cake and slathered all over that cake, was *my sauce*. Hot diggity! A no-fat chocolate torte. With its own chocolate sauce!

We gathered round the adorable thing, spoons flying. It was a dark chocolate truffle of a cake, smothered in the deepest, fudgiest sauce ever tasted by mortals. We elbowed for position, spooning up sauce-dripping chunks of torte as fast as we could. Soon it was gone and the plate was scraped clean. I tried to repeat it, carefully giving it a full 6 minutes with no stirring. Eureka! Another sauced cake.

For someone who makes her living developing sybaritic low-fat recipes, a discovery like this is a gift from Valhalla. Or Mount Olympus. Or wherever. In *somebody's* Pantheon, there has to be a goddess of chocolate, and she probably has to watch her weight constantly. Perhaps *she* sent it.

Strategy For Making Puddle Cakes

Keep puddle cake staples: low-fat unsweetened cocoa powder, cornflour, sugar and skimmed milk powder, in air-tight, well-labelled canisters on a shelf near the microwave. Keep the bottle of natural vanilla essence near by as well. Invest in a couple of sets of American-style measuring scoops. They are very inexpensive, and available in many cookware or hardware shops and departments (or see Mail Order Guide, page 192). Keep the appropriate scoop in the appropriate canister: ½-cup scoop in the cocoa; ½-cup scoop in the sugar; ⅓-cup scoop in the skimmed milk powder; ¼-cup scoop in the cornflour. (For those who do not have a set of these scoops, I give the measurements in tablespoons as well.)

The cakes are all cooked in a 3½pt/2 l 7-inch/18-cm top diameter, opaque white-plastic measuring jug. Keep the jug, the sifter and the whisk together on the shelf with the canisters. Keep approx 18 fl oz/½ l boxes of longlife skimmed milk on the shelf too, along with a 1 pt/570 ml measuring jug that is marked in fluid ounces (for measuring the milk). With all this in place, it takes no time at all (and no thought) to make a puddle cake. Afterwards, be sure everything is put back in its proper place. And replenish things as they begin to get low.

As far as timing is concerned, these cakes have been developed in a 650 watt microwave oven. I have *tested* them in a wide variety of microwaves, of all sizes, makes and wattages, and the recipe does work in many 600 and 650 machines, but all I can say is: there are no hard-and-fast rules (see page 23). You must work out the timing for your particular machine. You may have to add an extra fluid ounce of milk and/or you may have to subtract a minute (or half a minute) from the cooking time.

188

All the Slim Cuisine microwave white sauces, the milk puddings, the chocolate sauces and the puddle cake, call for an opaque, white plastic, 3½ pt/2 l measuring jug. Even if the sticker on the jug warns, 'not for use in the microwave', you may use it in these recipes without fear. I checked with the manufacturer; problems arise when the jug is left in the microwave for too long a period of time, and the plastic melts. In all the Slim Cuisine recipes utilizing the jug, the time is far too short for such problems to arise.

⧖ ⬚ ⊠ CHOCOLATE TRUFFLE TORTE WITH CHOCOLATE SAUCE

⏲15 minutes

Here is the sublime accident. It tastes best, I believe, when it has cooled somewhat, but it is almost impossible to fend people off long enough for it to cool. It even tastes wonderful on the second and third day, but you're on your own trying to save it that long. The texture is very dense and the sauce is thick and dark, so it tastes extraordinarily rich – as if it were Mississippi Mud Cake, or Chocolate Decadence, or even Death by Chocolate, all infamously fattening, waistline-destroying chocolate tortes. (In fact, unless they have actually seen this torte being made, people refuse to believe that it is a very low-fat cake. And even then, they suspect sleight of hand.) My current favourite dinner-party trick is to excuse myself after the main course and retire to the kitchen to prepare the dessert. Of course, everyone follows me. In minutes, I whip up the batter and make the cake. When it slides out of the jug and settles on to the plate, cloaked with sauce and wreathed with aromatic steam, everyone gasps with amazed admiration. While it cools, I rustle up some ice cream in the processor (see page 171) and everyone gasps some more. Each guest gets a wedge of torte, a puddle of sauce, a scoop of ice cream and (in season) a scattering of raspberries. Once you have mastered the torte in your particular microwave and the ice cream in your processor, try the combination at your next dinner party.

½ cup (7 tablespoons) low-fat, unsweetened cocoa powder (see Mail Order Guide, page 192)
½ cup (7 tablespoons) castor sugar
⅓ cup (5 tablespoons) skimmed milk powder

¼ cup (3 tablespoons) cornflour
½ teaspoon natural vanilla essence
8 fl oz/225 ml skimmed milk

1   Sift the cocoa, sugar, milk powder and cornflour into a 3½ pt/2 l, 7-inch/18-cm top diameter, opaque, white-plastic measuring jug (see box, page 189).

2   With a wire whisk, thoroughly whisk the vanilla essence and milk into the dry ingredients. Cover the jug with microwave cling film.

3   Microwave on full power for 6 minutes.

4   Remove from the microwave, pierce the cling film to release the steam, remove the cling film, set the jug on a rack and allow to sit for 5 minutes.

5   Carefully loosen the torte all around and underneath with a palette knife. Put a plate over the jug, turn it over and let the torte gently slide out on to the plate. It will be covered with a perfectly delightful chocolate sauce. Spoon out any sauce remaining in the jug and dribble it over the torte. Let the torte cool at room temperature.

Note: Sometimes, as these tortes slide out of their jug, they perform a leisurely somersault, and land on the plate with the sauce underneath instead of on top. If this should happen, simply put a plate on top, reverse, and spoon any sauce that remains on the first plate over the torte.

Mail Order Guide

Anton's Delicatessen
101 Hare lane
Claygate
Esher
Surrey
KT10 0QX

Tel: 0372 462306

Balsamic vinegar
Dry-pack sun-dried tomatoes
Quick-cooking polenta
Pure vanilla essence

Cambridge Continental Store
9 The Broadway
Mill Road
Cambridge
CB1 3AH

Tel: 0223 248069

Balsamic vinegar
Dry-pack sun-dried tomatoes
Quick-cooking polenta

Culpeper Limited
Hadstock Road
Linton
Cambridgeshire
CB1 6NJ

Tel: 0223 894054

Divertimenti
139–41 Fulham Road
South Kensington
London
SW3

Tel: 071 581 8065

Health Craze
Cromwell Court
115 Earls Court Road
London
SW5

Tel: 071 244 7784

Parson's Trading Limited
PO Box 995
Purton
Swindon
Wiltshire
SN5 9WB

Tel: 0793 772200

Californian dry-pack sun-dried
tomatoes, no added salt
Pure vanilla essence

American-style graduated
measuring scoops

Balsamic vinegar
Quick-cooking polenta
Vegetable stock powders
including Friggs Vegetal

Low-fat, unsweetened cocoa
powder

Index

Note: Recipes for soups, main courses, salads and breads suitable for vegetarians are shown with an asterisk.